THE PAE LIVING BUILDING:
Developer-Led, Nature-Inspired

An Ecotone Publishing Book/2022
Copyright ©2022 Mary Adam Thomas

Ecotone Publishing — an Imprint of International Living Future Institute

For more information write:

Ecotone Publishing
1501 East Madison Street Suite 150
Seattle, WA 98122

Author: Mary Adam Thomas
Book Design: Johanna Björk, softfirm
Edited by: Fred McLennan

Library of Congress Control Number: 2021945396
Library of Congress Cataloging-in Publication Data

ISBN 978-1-7362129-0-5

1. ARCHITECTURE   2. ENVIRONMENT   3. PHILOSOPHY

First Edition

Printed in Canada on FSC-certified paper, processed Chlorine-Free, using vegetable-based inks.

THE PAE LIVING BUILDING

Developer-Led, Nature-Inspired

LIVING
BUILDING
CHALLENGE

FOREWORD

BY DENIS HAYES

In its Darwinian pursuit of the survival of the fittest, Nature places its highest value on energy efficiency. If the cheetah spends more calories catching the zebra than it can obtain from the zebra as food, the cheetah will perish. Energy efficiency is the engine of evolution.

For some peculiar reason, early in our pre-history, humans became enamored of the exact opposite of efficiency: conspicuous gluttony. In poor countries and rich lands alike, humans bestow status on those who show off their wastefulness.

For example, America's legacy automobile manufacturers and most EV start-ups focus their keenest interest on sports utility vehicles and light trucks. Eight of the ten top-selling motor vehicles in the United States in 2020 (including all the top five) were SUVs and trucks. One hundred-fifty pound people impress their neighbors by driving 6,000 pound vehicles — behemoths so huge that they can be perilous to navigate — to the grocery store to get a loaf of bread.

Mother Nature ultimately weeds such behaviors out of the gene pool.

Even where wasting energy is not flaunted, however, it is generally ignored. When tenants are choosing a building to lease, the rent is frequently 25-30 times larger than the energy bills. There is little pressure on landlords to make their buildings energy-efficient. So most don't. Virtually all buildings are built to code, which means they are as inefficient as they can be without breaking the law.

With increasing attention now being paid to the climate crisis, some buildings are designed to be obviously "green." In energy terms, this generally means that they have installed solar panels on their roofs, planted grass and shrubs on terraces, and placed bicycle racks out front. These features are considered sexy; energy efficiency, on the other hand, is a boring soporific.

In fact, hyper-efficiency is complex and difficult. The cheetah's astonishing acceleration, which enables it to catch its prey in a flash, is possible because its back flexes and extends, allowing its rear feet (with non-retractable claws acting as runner's cleats) to reach far ahead of its front feet when they strike the ground. Evolution's quest for the most efficient solution produced a cheetah that is a marvel of bioengineering.

Sweeping advances in energy efficiency are among the many remarkable achievements that make the PAE Living Building a marvel of engineering. It is designed to use less than one-fifth as much energy per square foot as comparable buildings in Portland.

What's more, its developers, architects, engineers, and contractors accomplished this within the constraints of a historic preservation district and a for-profit developer model. To simply look at the PAE Living Building from the street, you would never guess how special it is. It does not replace conspicuous consumption with conspicuous frugality. Superficially, it resembles every other building in its neighborhood. Yet, in terms of performance, the PAE Living Building is in a whole different league.

Because buildings currently use 76 percent of all electricity in the United States, they are key to the rapid transformation to an electrified economy. If all American buildings used as little energy per square foot as the PAE Living Building, the nation would have abundant surplus electricity to meet our transportation and industry needs.

Since life first emerged on earth 3.5 billion years ago, nature has been beta testing myriad strategies. Natural selection is a shorthand way of saying that not everything is equally likely to survive and produce offspring. Those best adapted to thrive in their environment will dominate tomorrow's world. And the incontrovertible lesson is that the most efficient solution always prevails.

The PAE Living Building is a paragon of efficiency. It uses far less energy, less water, and less material than other buildings while delivering superior levels of comfort, lighting, and productivity.

Every report from the International Panel on Climate Change is more dire than the one that preceded it. The climate crisis has now arrived. We are out of time to remove carbon-based fuels from the global economy.

In order to make a swift transition to a carbon-free future, it is crucial that we dramatically upgrade the efficiency of our built environment. The PAE Living Building offers living proof that what is necessary is also possible.

ACKNOWLEDGEMENTS

This book came to life in sync with the very building it describes. Both projects took shape during the surreal era of 2020/2021, when the world felt upside down and inside out. Having previously written about Living Buildings, I know how difficult they are to accomplish, even in the best of circumstances. But the remarkable people who created the PAE Living Building encountered unprecedented obstacles far beyond the sizeable ones faced by every team that aspires to the world's most stringent green building standard. In the midst of managing would-be obstructions, they also adapted to the various factors that disrupted all aspects of life during that stretch of time. I appreciate how everyone I contacted during my research for this book cheerfully accommodated the sometimes frustrating nature of virtual communications, especially for large group interviews. I look forward to a time when we can stand together at the PAE Living Building, celebrating face-to-face rather than screen-to-screen.

I am enormously grateful to PAE's incomparable leader, Paul Schwer, for entrusting me with this story. It was a responsibility I took very seriously, even in the midst of – or perhaps because of – the laughs we shared along the way. I am also indebted to the core project team members from PAE, ZGF Architects, Walsh Construction Co., Edlen & Co., KPFF, Biohabitats, Brightworks, RDH, Apex Real Estate Partners, and Downtown Development Group. Thank you all for generously making time for me over the course of many calls, many meetings, many emails, and many follow-up requests. Your insights are as abundant as your talents. To PAE's Sarah Fischer: Thank you for your stellar cat-herding skills, which kept us organized and on track.

To the extremely long list of people who helped conceive, plan, design, build, permit, or otherwise deliver the PAE Living Building: Thank you for adding a beautiful new bloom to the built environment. Regardless of whether you are quoted or referred to in the pages of this book, your game-changing work stands for itself. You inspire me and others to do what we can to make a difference.

It's an honor to have the (fore)words of the esteemed Denis Hayes sit beside my own in these pages. I had the great privilege of working closely with Denis while researching and writing *The Greenest Building*, and the experience remains a career highlight. Thank you, Denis, for elevating this book with your perspective and eloquence.

I owe a mountain of thanks to Ecotone's Michael Berrisford, who ushered me through yet another complex assignment with grace, professionalism, and a delightful sense of humor. Michael: Thank you for serving as this book's spirit guide. I always enjoy our collaborations and this was certainly no exception. Thank you, too, to Living Future Hero Fred McLennan, whose editing expertise helped keep every stage of the manuscript clean and crisp. And, of course, to Johanna Björk, who has once again used her superpowers to wrap my written content in an elegant design.

Lastly, I'm grateful to those who kept me in balance during the bizarre experience of writing a book while muddling through a pandemic. Thanks to my sisters for maintaining a constant stream of therapeutic group texts, to my parents for figuring out how to Zoom, to Deborah for always knowing what I mean even when words are hard, to Mackenzie and Reed for coming home again and insisting on occasional dance parties, and to Kevin for being my hands-down favorite lockdown partner. You're all among the many blessings I'm oh-so-lucky to be able to count.

MARY ADAM THOMAS

AUTHOR PROFILE

MARY ADAM THOMAS

Mary Adam Thomas is an independent writer and editor who has proudly helped spread the word about the Living Building Challenge since its 2006 debut.

This is her third contribution to the Living Building Challenge Series. Her earlier titles include *The Greenest Building: How the Bullitt Center Changes the Urban Landscape* and *Building in Bloom: The Making of the Center for Sustainable Landscapes at Phipps Conservatory and Botanical Gardens*. She is also the author of *The Living Building Challenge: Roots and Rise of the World's Greenest Standard*.

Mary collaborated with Jason F. McLennan on his collection of essays, *Zugunruhe: The Inner Migration to Profound Environmental Change* and wrote the introduction to McLennan's follow-up book, *Transformational Thought: Radical Ideas to Remake the Built Environment*. In addition, she provided substantial editorial support for *Living Building Makers* by Jonathan A. Wright, *Living Building Education: The Evolution of Bertschi School's Science Wing* by Chris Hellstern, and *Busby: Architecture's New Edges* by Peter Busby – all published by Ecotone. Mary is also the collaborative author, with Andrew Schorr, of *The Web-Savvy Patient: An Insider's Guide to Navigating the Internet When Facing Medical Crisis*.

Mary works from various cozy corners of her Pacific Northwest home, which she shares with her husband. If not at her keyboard, she is most likely seeking out a water view or sharing food, wine, and laughter with family and friends.

PART I

The Leading Edge

A Firm Grasp of What is Possible

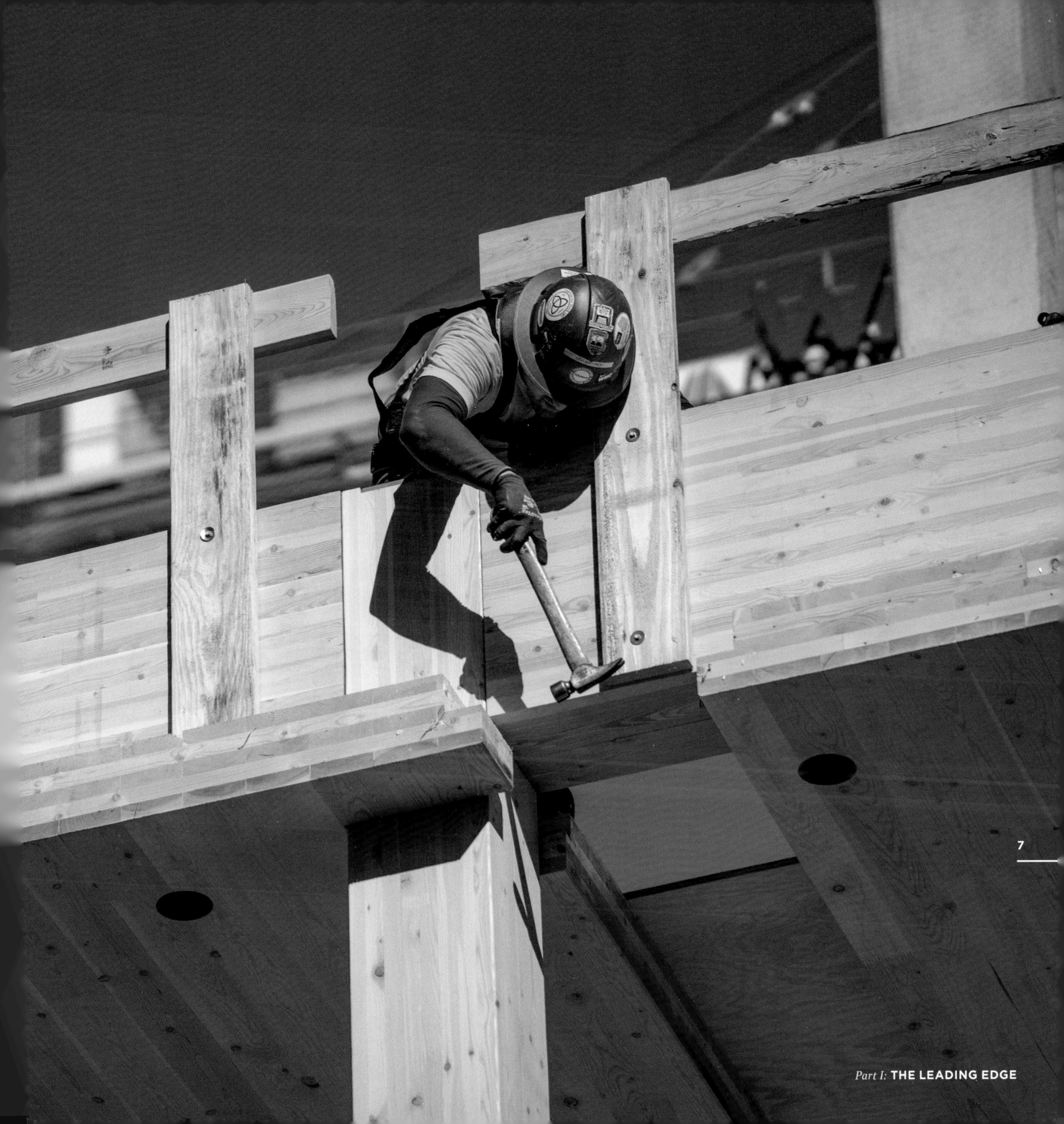

THE PAE LIVING BUILDING: *Developer-Led, Nature-Inspired*

MAKING CHANGE

It all comes down to this: PAE is in business to help solve our planet's energy and water challenges. This message is not just spelled out in the firm's marketing materials; it is integral to every project that bears the PAE stamp. The people of PAE embody this mission because they believe wholeheartedly in it. The firm has been on the leading edge of sustainable engineering innovation since the beginning.

PAE's origin story dates back to 1967 when Harold "Pete" Peterson and two partners (Sid Nielsen and Dan Pickett) formed Peterson Associated Engineers, Portland, Oregon's first integrated mechanical-electrical engineering firm. In the decades that followed, PAE's growth ebbed and flowed along with the local and national economies while in-house leaders continued to seek ways for the firm to remain on the leading innovative edge.

In 1994, a young mechanical engineer named Paul Schwer arrived in Portland from New York City looking for a change. He found it at

PAE, which was rebounding from the turbulent 1980s, a boom-and-not-quite-bust period for the firm that yielded important lessons about the benefits of diversifying its client base. Schwer was welcomed by PAE's then-president, Carl Urben, who had taken the reins upon Peterson's retirement in 1982. By that time, PAE had built a reputation as the go-to shop when project teams were facing head-scratching engineering problems and tackling difficult building types. Schwer, a self-described "energy geek," was up for the challenge and settled right in.

9

"PAE and Portland have something very important in common. Like this city, our company is fundamentally optimistic about the possibilities of a cleaner, greener society."

MARC BRUNE
PAE

"For the 2002 white paper, we went out to the year 2050 and backcasted what a perfect building would be, following a process called the Natural Step, which was big for a while. That paper really got me thinking about what to do when LEED is not enough; when you want to do more than just be 30 percent better than code. I wanted to know what the end game was, especially for energy."

PAUL SCHWER
PAE

By the end of the 1990s, so-called "green" design and construction sensibilities were taking hold. The U.S. Green Building Council (USGBC) introduced the first version of its flagship initiative in 1998: the Leadership in Energy and Environmental Design (LEED) green building rating and certification system, with richer versions to follow in the next few years. Meanwhile, other programs emerged — in the United States and globally — that also sought to standardize and incentivize environmentally-friendly approaches to the built environment. Architects, engineers, builders, developers, and entrepreneurs were pondering how to tilt their work in this intriguing and increasingly important new direction.

Schwer was among them. Encouraged by PAE leadership, he joined forces with a group of like-minded Portland-based industry professionals to consider not only what a greener built environment would look like, but also what it would take to design and engineer it using the "backcasting" method. They formed a task force affiliated with the Oregon Natural Step Network and originally organized by Jeanne Roy of the Northwest Earth Institute, ultimately publishing a 2002 white paper, "Using the Natural Step as a Framework Toward the Construction and Operation of Fully Sustainable Buildings."

The white paper was prophetic in several ways. For one, it proposed an approach remarkably similar to what became the Living Building Challenge (which was still an idea percolating in the mind of Jason F. McLennan years before its formal launch in 2006). Also, several of the paper's authors came from firms that would later collaborate on the PAE Living Building. One of those was Dennis Wilde of Gerding Edlen (Edlen & Co.'s predecessor company). Dennis was a passionate early advocate of sustainable design and brought a deep knowledge of both construction and development to the group. (See sidebar.)

THE OREGON NATURAL STEP NETWORK TASK FORCE

Authors of the 2002 white paper "Using the Natural Step as a Framework Toward the Construction and Operation of Fully Sustainable Buildings"

Duke Castle
The Castle Group

Logan Cravens
SERA Architects

Patrick Driscoll
Walsh Construction Co.

John Echlin
SERA Architects

Paul Schwer
PAE Consulting Engineers, Inc

Alan Scott
PGE Green Building Services

Charles Stephens
Oregon Dept. of Energy

Dennis Wilde
Gerding Edlen Development

ENGINEERING DISTINCTION

By the time Schwer was named PAE president in 2004, both he and the firm had solidified their dedication to environmentally-responsible and even regenerative design. PAE began proudly presenting itself as a triple bottom line company committed to people, planet, and profit.

Employee rosters grew steadily and, by 2015, the company had offices in four cities: Portland, Oregon; Seattle, Washington; San Francisco, California; and Eugene, Oregon.

Key to this growth and expansion was the firm's critical role in helping to create its Seattle home, the Bullitt Center. PAE served as mechanical and electrical engineers as well as energy modelers while Luma Lighting Design, a PAE subsidiary, offered its specialized expertise for this revolutionary Living Building — the first commercial office building and largest (at that time) structure ever to achieve Living Building Challenge certification. After the Bullitt Center opened its doors in 2013, PAE moved in as a tenant, initially occupying approximately 3,000 of the building's 52,000 square feet and later occupying the entire third and fourth floors. Other pilot tenants included the Bullitt Foundation (the building's owner), the International Living Future Institute (the non-profit that oversees and administers the Living Building Challenge), and Luma Lighting Design.

11

PAE employees lucky enough to work in the Bullitt Center did not take the privilege for granted. It was quickly apparent to firm leadership that recruiting and retaining its Seattle-based talent came more easily. The word was getting out that getting hired for a position in that office meant working in a Living Building, itself a showcase of cutting-edge mechanical and electrical engineering. So operating out of a Living Building became more than just a way to live PAE's values; it became a measurably advantageous strategy.

The next logical (albeit ambitious) step: moving the company's Portland headquarters into a Living Building. The only problem was that there had yet to be a fully certified Living Building of any typology constructed in the City of Roses. So if PAE was going to run its central operations out of a Living Building, it would have to grow one of its own.

This would offer a new opportunity to walk the firm's talk. PAE was already intimately familiar with the Living Building Challenge — its value as well as its rigor and risks — and touted the need to add more Living Buildings to the landscape. Given the success of the Bullitt Center, which proved what was possible for a regenerative commercial structure, PAE was well equipped to raise this green bar.

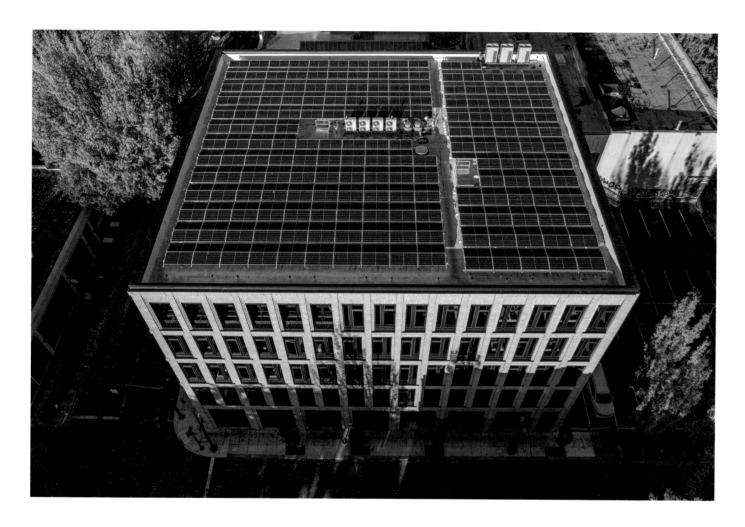

DUE DILIGENCE

Early research into the feasibility of investing in and building a PAE Living headquarters began in March 2016.

Schwer and two of his fellow PAE principals, Scott Bevan and Dave Williams, met with prominent local developer Mark Edlen, co-founder of Gerding Edlen.* (PAE had previously collaborated with Gerding Edlen on numerous projects, most notably the Oregon Sustainability Center, Portland's first attempt at a developer-led Living Building effort. Although that project did not ever get off the ground, its spirit and many of its intended performance strategies live on in the PAE Living Building.) The goal of that first meeting was simple: PAE wanted to better understand the fundamentals of Portland commercial real

"When I asked Jill Sherman, Mark Edlen, and Greg Goodman what it would take to get started, they said, 'All it takes is a handshake.' So we all shook hands and got to work on what would become the PAE Living Building."

PAUL SCHWER
PAE

* Gerding Edlen Development reorganized in 2021, at which point Edlen & Co. was formed and became the developer of record and co-investor for this project.

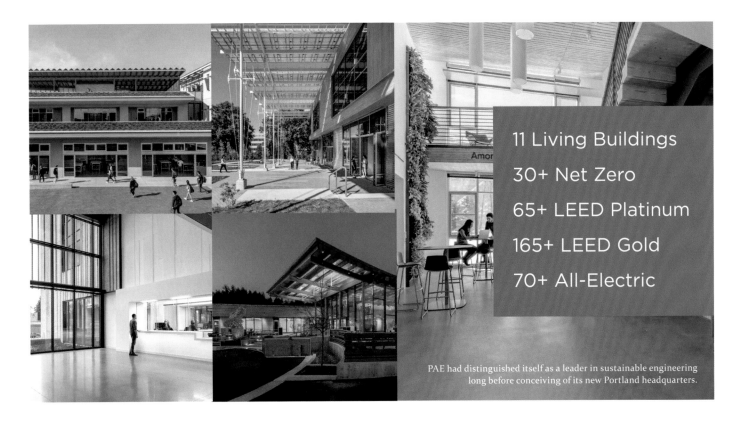

11 Living Buildings

30+ Net Zero

65+ LEED Platinum

165+ LEED Gold

70+ All-Electric

PAE had distinguished itself as a leader in sustainable engineering long before conceiving of its new Portland headquarters.

estate ownership, including typical turnaround times, lease rates, cost ratios, location strategies, etcetera.

PAE was encouraged enough by what they learned in the March 2016 meeting to keep moving forward. That meeting led to follow-ups with other prospective project partners — Apex Real Estate Partners and the Downtown Development Group among them — with each new conversation helping turn the theoretical project into something that slowly began to take on a realistic shape. By March 2017, the project partners were considering site options. By August of that year, they had committed to the location at SW 1st Avenue and SW Pine Street, with PAE serving as anchor tenant in a structure that had yet to be designed.

From there, it was up to PAE to establish its own financial and environmental parameters for the project. The firm's leadership team met in October 2017 to discuss the possibility of investing their own fees in the project and asking other members of the team to do the same, which would be a significant pledge but would further demonstrate PAE's willingness to stretch beyond

typical boundaries for this effort. The idea was unanimously approved. (For more details on the project's innovative financial story, see Part II.)

In an April 2018 meeting, the leadership identified the overarching goals for the project in order of importance:

1. Achieve Living Building Challenge Petal Certification for Energy

2. Achieve Petal Certification for Water

3. Achieve U.S. Resiliency Council Silver Rating (for seismic resilience)

4. Achieve Full Living Building Certification

5. Achieve WELL Building Certification

6. Achieve LEED Platinum Certification

7. Achieve Passive House Certification

Downtown Seattle as seen from beneath the solar canopy at the Bullitt Center.

In the end, the leadership decided to focus exclusively on full Living Building certification and set aside the potentially distracting work of pursuing the other certifications.

Three key points helped secure the project's Living Building goal: 1) a PAE Living Building would support and reduce the cost of recruitment, 2) it would aid in staff retention, and 3) it would enhance the health and productivity of its employees. In other words, the endeavor would serve each of the elements of the firm's triple bottom line: people, planet, and profit.

By summer 2018, a few important details had yet to be determined — the precise specifications of the building, the makeup of its occupants, the roster of professionals who would help it come to life, and the particulars of its financial strategy. Nonetheless, the firm and its project partners had committed to this audacious undertaking, opening the proverbial door to the structure that would ultimately not only house PAE, but define it.

"There's a significant cost that comes with recruiting new people and significant benefits that come with retaining them once they're here. Working in a sustainably designed building, especially a Living Building with elements of biophilia, makes it easier to recruit and retain staff. It's hard to exactly quantify the data, but it's real. Recruitment and retention helped make the valid business case to the PAE leadership as they considered investing in a Living Building for our home office."

MARC BRUNE
PAE

"Employees today are looking for a job that provides more than a nice paycheck and benefits. People want to work for an organization that has a higher purpose, beyond the bottom line. The PAE Living Building ties the core values and mission of our organization — people, planet, and profit — with the intrinsic motivations of our employees."

SHILOH BUTTERWORTH
PAE

"My personal commitment to sustainability — specifically, minimizing the harmful effects that buildings have on the environment — has been a key driver in my career and it's why I wanted to work for Gerding Edlen in the first place. From the start, this firm's founders approached real estate development with an environmentalist's perspective and they've always been willing to innovate. They were doing green buildings before there was LEED, then doing more LEED projects than anyone else and always pushing the boundaries. Now, we understand that sustainability isn't just about the environment; it's also about community. That's why Edlen & Co. was formed: to focus on amplifying both our environmental and community impact. And that's why I love what I do."

JILL SHERMAN
Edlen & Co.

15

PART II

Getting Ready

Planning for the Future,
Accommodating the Present

18

THE PAE LIVING BUILDING: *Developer-Led, Nature-Inspired*

"Without the whole team's dedication to that common goal, it's easy for projects to slip from Living Building to LEED Platinum or Gold or Silver, all the way to 'We'll just do a green building and call it good.' That never happened on this team. Everyone worked together toward that end."

PAUL SCHWER
PAE

"Paul didn't start the conversation with any of us by saying that we were going to try to build a Living Building. He said, 'We are going to build a Living Building.' The idea of not making it just wasn't an option."

KATHY BERG
ZGF Architects

"At the end of the day, a group of stubborn and determined people who are all working toward the same North Star are pretty hard to defeat."

ED SLOOP
WALSH

"The level of mutual respect and trust shared by the members of this team was critical in pulling off this project. We set out to do something that none of us had ever done before and there were so many unknowns. But it worked because of this collaboration. Now we have a great building that's going to contribute to the community, and that's really satisfying."

JILL SHERMAN
Edlen & Co.

A SINGULAR FOCUS

Once PAE set its sights on the Living Building Challenge for its Portland headquarters, there was never a question about whether the project would aim for full certification, meeting every Imperative of all seven Petals. Like every Living Building project that came before it, the PAE Building would be a spectacularly difficult undertaking. Plus, it would have the added challenge of being the first developer-led Living Building. But nothing less than official Living status would do.

Assembling the right team, then, would be critical. Every designer, engineer, builder, project manager, subcontractor, funder, and support person needed to understand this shared goal and embrace all that was involved to achieve it, both individually and as a group. Yes, there would be headwinds, as there are on every project. But the right people would know how to navigate through them.

ASSEMBLING THE TEAM

Selecting the right partners came more easily on this effort than it might have on a traditional project or even on another Living Building.

To start with, most of the members of the core team would also need to be willing and able to provide services in exchange for an equity stake in the building in order for the financial plan to work. (See the "Ownership and Financing" section of this chapter for more details on this aspect of the story.) This equity arrangement changed the typical hierarchy; there would be no need to explain things up the chain of command as the project progressed, since the owners were active participants in the planning process and intimately familiar with the nuances of the Challenge. Plus, it made sense to approach partners from the RMI team roster, as PAE had already established a powerful rapport with ZGF Architects and KPFF from that effort. As such, the key players who would support PAE in its role as mechanical and electrical engineers emerged relatively quickly. PAE selected Edlen & Co. first and together the two firms selected the rest of the team.

DEVELOPER: EDLEN & CO.

Edlen & Co., which emerged from the 2021 reorganization of Gerding Edlen, has a well-earned reputation in Portland and nationally as a leader in sustainable real estate development. This made them the clear choice for the PAE Living Building. PAE knew they were in good hands with the experienced and talented Jill Sherman, an Edlen & Co. partner, with whom they had worked on numerous projects in the 15 years prior.

ARCHITECTS: ZGF

As PAE and Edlen & Co. pondered design partners, they chose not to distribute an RFP to local architecture firms. For one thing, they knew all too well the extensive time and resources required to assemble proposals for projects of this type and they did not want to put PAE clients through that process. Secondly, the architecture firm chosen for the PAE Living Building would also need to serve as investors in the project, which narrowed the list of eligible firms. Finally, PAE and Edlen & Co. needed to have an existing rapport with the project's design partners. Given these factors, ZGF emerged as the obvious choice.

"It was interesting to observe the design process for our building with members of the ownership group always present as part of the design team. We did all the same analysis as we would for another Living Building project and maybe more, but didn't have to develop the same deliverables to explain our approaches to solving the energy or natural ventilation problems because the decision makers were part of the design process." **MARC BRUNE,** PAE

"There was a level of trust among all of us that I think was critical to the outcome. We were all committed to the same thing: making a Living Building and doing it using a developer model. We knew that even though we might at times disagree about different attributes of design, we had the same intent in mind. We did well because we really trust each other professionally and personally."

JUSTIN BROOKS
ZGF Architects

"We don't put our land in for sustainable projects because it's good for our resume; we do it because it's in the best interest of Portland. Our mentality is: A rising tide raises all boats. That's the main driver."

GREG GOODMAN
Downtown Development Group

"Unlike in Seattle, Portland doesn't have world-famous large corporations. That's not what we're known for. But now we can say we're home to the largest mixed-use sustainable building in the world. I'm proud of Apex for being partners in it."

NATHAN SASAKI
Apex Real Estate Partners

"Mike Steffen is probably one of the best people in our industry in terms of understanding the science of building skins and knowing what types will last forever. He's an architect himself; he literally teaches architects how to do this stuff. And Ed Sloop's passion for his work is obvious. So WALSH was a great choice."

PAUL SCHWER
PAE

BUILDERS: WALSH CONSTRUCTION CO.

Of the two local builders on the shortlist, WALSH stood out for a few reasons. For one, PAE and Edlen & Co. had proved the firms' ability to work well together. But it was the powerful pairing of WALSH's Chief Estimator Ed Sloop and Director of Innovation Mike Steffen that helped seal the deal. While Sloop impressed PAE with his meticulous attention to detail, Steffen displayed his superior knowledge of building science, particularly with regard to high-performing façades.

STRUCTURAL & CIVIL ENGINEERS: KPFF CONSULTING ENGINEERS

Their valuable contributions to the RMI project proved KPFF's ability to take on the PAE Living Building, with Principal Anne Monnier more than ably leading the effort. With more than 40 years of successful collaborations behind them, PAE and KPFF had a reliable foundation of experience and mutual trust to draw from.

LANDOWNER: DOWNTOWN DEVELOPMENT GROUP

The Downtown Development Group (DDG) and the Edlen organization have a long and fruitful history of collaborating on efforts to "green up" Portland's downtown built environment. So when Edlen & Co. brought the PAE Living Building opportunity to them, DDG knew that offering its land as a form of investment was the right thing to do.

WATER TREATMENT: BIOHABITATS

Biohabitats' Pete Muñoz had contributed his expertise to the Bullitt Center project, which provided PAE with a clear sense of the firm's (and Muñoz's) skills when it came to water treatment and reuse strategies. Since that time, the two firms had worked together on a variety of projects, making Biohabitats the natural choice for the PAE Living Building.

LEASING AGENT: APEX REAL ESTATE PARTNERS

Apex Real Estate Partners, led by Executive Director Nathan Sasaki, was eager to help put the PAE Living Building on the map in Portland. Sasaki had served as PAE's real estate broker for more than a decade by the time this project began, so the firm knew they could draw on his deep understanding of the Portland commercial real estate market. Serving as the broker for the PAE Living Building's commercial spaces, Apex embraced the opportunity to help distinguish Portland and its downtown core.

"We already fundamentally trusted ZGF, and we knew they were financially strong enough to be able to invest their fees in the project. Plus, they're just a kick-ass team to work with."

PAUL SCHWER
PAE

"I grew up in Europe and I'm used to buildings that have been around for hundreds of years. I've never understood why buildings in the United States are often expected to have a 50-year life. There's no reason (barring extreme events) that the PAE Living Building can't be around for 500 years; we created a structural frame that will allow it to."

ANNE MONNIER
KPFF

"The distance to daylight and ventilation that we were trying to accomplish was right in line with the rest of the historic neighborhood. And traditional historic materials were for the most part non-toxic. So we had a lot of interesting 'looking backwards while looking forward' moments on this project."

KATHY BERG
ZGF Architects

NON-NEGOTIABLES

Design meetings began in earnest in March 2018. The team had no need for a formal design charrette to kick things off, as all players knew from the outset the over-arching objective: accomplish the 20 Imperatives incorporated into the seven performance area Petals of Living Building Challenge 3.1.

Beyond rising to meet the Challenge, the team also wanted the PAE Living Building to achieve these goals:

STAND FOR 500 YEARS
The building needed to be designed and constructed for both endurance and adaptability. These qualities would contribute not only to the structure's longevity but also help make the business case for its longstanding value as a mixed-use commercial venture. While the building itself would be structurally flexible, it would also need to offer a flexible floorplan capable of adapting to and evolving with the needs of its occupants. As an aspirational 500-year building, it was intended to cater to multiple generations of users.

HONOR THE NEIGHBORHOOD
The building needed to reflect the personality and architectural traditions of historic Skidmore/Old Town Portland. While mapping out the plans, ZGF designers were pleased to find that window heights and proportions in the nearby historic structures would naturally support daylighting strategies, so complementing them would not mean sacrificing energy efficiency. Plus, few Red List materials existed when 18th-century buildings were constructed, so the designers could provide specifications for masonry, stone, and wood to stay in harmony with the local design aesthetic while meeting Living Building Challenge Materials Petal requirements.

MEET THE 2050 RENEWABLE ENERGY TARGET
In 2017, the City of Portland and Multnomah County announced a commitment to transition all community energy sources to renewables by 2050. The PAE Living Building would end up being a dramatic and nearly-30-years-ahead-of-schedule case study of what can be done to reach that goal. The building's designers now hope the project will stand as a Living laboratory that inspires other developers, designers, and builders to follow suit to help the city meet its important objective.

"We decided not to push the emergency operations center idea with the city because we found another way to raise the funds we needed. Still, I think it's a viable option for other seismically sound projects to pursue. It's a modest investment for the city to know they have a building they can use when they need it."

PAUL SCHWER
PAE

Artist Toma Villa's wood carving stands in the ground-floor lobby of the building.

IDEAS SET ASIDE

As plans progressed, certain concepts were presented, hashed out, and eventually dismissed for practical or financial reasons.

INCLUDING A RESIDENTIAL COMPONENT

Edlen & Co. devoted substantial time researching the feasibility of reserving a portion of the square footage for residential rental units. They plugged different scenarios into the pro forma, exploring both market rate and affordable housing models. In the end, however, the idea was abandoned due to concerns related not just to cost, but also to water and energy usage.

SERVING AS AN EMERGENCY OPERATIONS CENTER

Early on, Schwer spoke with Portland Mayor Ted Wheeler to explore the idea of having PAE vacate its own three floors and allow the city to use the space for six months as a command center in the wake of a major earthquake. Given the planned seismic resiliency of the structure, as well as its on-site energy, water, and waste infrastructure, it would likely be one of the few reliably safe places where such operations could be headquartered. In exchange, PAE asked the city for a nominal annual "virtual" lease. However, the building's pro forma ended up penciling out without the extra income and the city never fully took to the idea so it was taken off the table.

BUILT-IN RESILIENCE

For the PAE Living Building to accomplish its mission of being a self-sufficient, biomimicking, 500-year structure, it needed inherent resilience.

The team wanted the PAE Living Building to stand as a durable symbol of strength in the heart of the city, not only for the benefit of its owners and occupants but also to help it serve as a lasting community asset.

ENERGY RESILIENCE

All Living Buildings are energy independent. The PAE Living Building is no exception. What gives this urban structure its considerable boost is a significant on-site battery, which supports its ability to operate even when untethered from the municipal power grid. Once PAE finalized the building's energy strategy, they ran calculations to determine how long the building could be "off the grid" while maintaining its average daily usage patterns throughout all 58,000 square feet. The answer: 100 days in summer when operated in low energy mode. In other words, the PAE Living Building has the capacity to function under its own power for an entire season regardless of the municipal utility's brownouts and blackouts that will likely become increasingly common in the coming decades. PAE hopes its new headquarters will serve as an example of what's possible with regard to energy independence for any urban building designed to endure the extremes of a changing climate. (For more on the building's battery, see the Energy Petal chapter.)

SEISMIC RESILIENCE

The PAE Living Building was intentionally designed, engineered, and built for maximum resilience in the event of a major earthquake (up to 8.0 on the Richter scale). After weighing various options, the team determined that it made both structural and financial sense to invest in a costlier "stiff" frame that would bring the building up to Category IV standards — achieving the same level of seismic resilience required of hospitals and fire stations. The more robust frame would sway less in an earthquake, which meant the building could sit closer to its historic neighbors without posing a threat. Thus, this decision to engineer the building for superior earthquake resilience provided the opportunity to expand the footprint on two sides of the building and gain an additional 208 square feet of leasable space spread out among all five floors. So the team was able to justify the additional one-time $135,000 construction expense by calculating into the pro forma the additional value created by the additional rentable square footage: approximately $150,000. Since that value was higher than the cost to upgrade the structure, they were able to include it in the project. Plus, this strategy would help the building stay safer in the midst of — and operational in the wake of — what might otherwise be a catastrophic seismic event.

"The seismic strategy was a result of this team putting our collective heads together rather than 'siloing' different approaches to solve the structural and cost challenges. Instead, we mixed them up and came up with an approach that solved two big problems. We did that with a lot of different design challenges in this building, which is very meaningful to me."

JUSTIN BROOKS
ZGF Architects

"The likelihood of a major Cascadia earthquake is something like 35 percent in the next 50 years. So for buildings built to code, you can turn that around and say there's a 35 percent chance they will be irreparably damaged and need to be torn down within 50 years. To me, it doesn't make any sense; there's no financial resilience to that."

MARC BRUNE
PAE

"If we don't do more Living Buildings, these sorts of historic districts will cease to exist because they'll become more and more susceptible to climate change-related disasters like flooding, wildfire, and other events. I think there's a broader sort of societal resilience — the things that make us who we are — that these buildings help support in the long run."

JUSTIN BROOKS
ZGF Architects

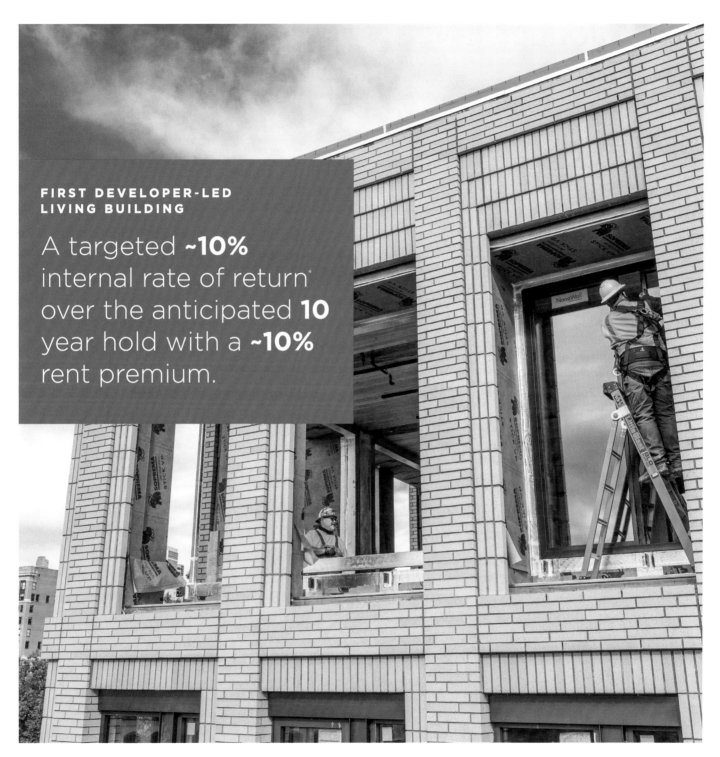

FIRST DEVELOPER-LED LIVING BUILDING

A targeted **~10%** internal rate of return* over the anticipated **10** year hold with a **~10%** rent premium.

*The project's targeted 10 year IRR was 10 percent. However, at the commencement of construction, the actual underwritten IRR was 8.3 percent.

OWNERSHIP
+ FINANCING

THE PAE LIVING BUILDING: *Developer-Led, Nature-Inspired*

"We're never going to get the kind of environmental performance we need all buildings to achieve unless and until we get the private sector to embrace net zero energy, net zero water, responsible materials sourcing, and carbon neutrality. And to do that, we have to get for-profit developers to see that being ultra-green can also be profitable. The PAE Living Building proves that the developer-led, privately financed model is possible, even while meeting the world's most rigorous green building standard."

JILL SHERMAN
Edlen & Co.

"If even one developer looks at our building and says, 'I can do this; I can create a Living Building and still make money for my investors,' that's a pretty big deal."

JUSTIN BROOKS
ZGF Architects

"A ten percent rent premium over a ten-year period with a ten percent levered internal rate of return. That's all it takes. If people think it's impossible, they only have to look at those three tens to see how simple it is to get yourself a Living Building."

PAUL SCHWER
PAE

Crews began working on the site in the spring of 2020.

A REPLICABLE DEVELOPER-LED FUNDING MODEL

The PAE Living Building set out to prove the viability of developing speculative mixed-use commercial structures that benefit their ecological and urban environments while delivering financial returns. For PAE, investing in the project and committing to serve as its anchor tenant was a way to live the firm's values.

But it was also a way to demonstrate to Portland — or any city, for that matter — what is possible in commercial development. Just as the Bullitt Center did in Seattle, the PAE Living Building aimed to raise this particular bar, showing investors that sustainable development can provide a modern, distinctive, competitive edge.

When the project began, there were 23 certified Living Buildings, 30 Petal-certified projects, and 59 Net Zero Energy Buildings certified by ILFI all around the world. In addition, there were an additional 550 projects that had registered with the Institute as aspirational Living Buildings. Of that collection, not one was a developer-led project that needed to deliver market-rate returns to its owners.

> "Ninety percent of the cash equity in the project came via opportunity zone investment, so it was really critical to raising the equity required for the project. For opportunity zone investors, the tax benefit is maximized by holding the investment for at least ten years. Our project needed to be looked at as a longer-term hold in order to achieve market rate returns. So the opportunity zone program was a perfect fit."

JILL SHERMAN
Edlen & Co.

> "Having spent the last 30 years developing over 80 high-performance LEED-certified buildings across the country, I view our Living Building as the pinnacle of my career and for our company as well. We have always believed that it is our responsibility to leave the world for our children and grandchildren better than we found it and I believe the PAE Living Building epitomizes that responsibility."

MARK EDLEN
Edlen & Co.

FOLLOWING THE MONEY

Traditional commercial buildings are typically funded with a combination of debt and equity and jointly owned by their investors, whose equity shares are based on the percentage of total equity required for the project.

Edlen & Co. led the effort to obtain the equity, loans, and other financing needed to make the nation's first developer-led Living Building a reality. The PAE Living Building was financed largely by traditional sources including a loan and investor equity, property assessed clean energy (PACE) financing, a couple of small grants for energy efficiency, and a small loan from Portland's redevelopment agency.

The construction and permanent loan was provided by First Interstate Bank at 54 percent of the building's cost, and was dependent on PAE's pre-lease of 71 percent of the building. Low interest PACE financing was used at 6 percent of the cost and, because of the building's sustainability and energy efficiency achievements, the project received two grants and a small loan from the city's redevelopment agency, equal in total to 2 percent of the building's cost.

Lastly, 38 percent of the cost came from equity investors which included the design/construction/development team (Edlen & Co., PAE, ZGF, WALSH, DDG, and Apex) and high net worth individuals. The development team invested their fees in-kind for a total of 18 percent of the cost, which not only minimized the financial risk to the project prior to its construction, but also decreased the amount of additional equity needed.

For PAE, ZGF, Edlen & Co., and Apex, this meant investing all of their professional fees. For DDG, it meant investing the value of the land on which the building would stand. WALSH invested some of its fees and also invested cash. In all, approximately half of the equity came from entities that were members of the project team, reducing the amount of outside equity that had to be raised and also giving these organizations seats at the owners' table.

The developers syndicated the remaining equity equal to 20 percent of the cost from high net worth individuals who were willing to take a lower projected rate of return based on: (1) the building being 71 percent pre-leased; (2) interest in owning a net zero building, i.e., ESG investment desire; (3) a high degree of lease-up confidence with the building being "state of the art" and net zero and its ability to attract and retain socially conscious tenants; and, (4) tax benefits of opportunity zone investment.

TWO WAYS TO OFFSET RENT PREMIUM

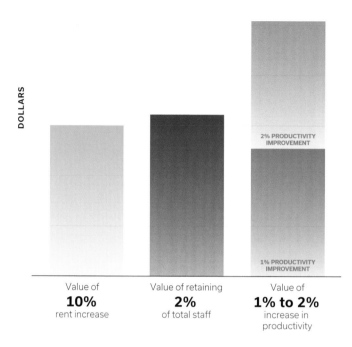

DOLLARS

2% PRODUCTIVITY
IMPROVEMENT

1% PRODUCTIVITY
IMPROVEMENT

Value of
10%
rent increase

Value of retaining
2%
of total staff

Value of
1% to 2%
increase in
productivity

The individual investors qualified for valuable tax benefits because the project is sited in an opportunity zone. (Following the passage of the Tax Cuts and Jobs Act of 2017, the U.S. Treasury designated opportunity zones throughout the country to encourage long-term investments through a federal tax incentive. The PAE Living Building is located in one of Oregon's 86 qualified opportunity zones.) The timing of this tax regulation was fortuitous, as Edlen & Co. was actively seeking cash investors for the PAE Living Building when it went into effect in 2018.

Edlen & Co. plugged all of these variables into the pro forma, while WALSH estimated the construction costs for the project. Those rough figures revealed much about what types of rents tenants could expect to pay and what types of returns investors could expect to collect. Knowing that there would be no out-of-pocket costs for the design fees or the land helped enormously in getting the project off the ground. The early commitments of the in-kind investors helped mitigate the risk for the third-party cash investors who otherwise would have likely seen this project as too risky to invest in early in the process.

INVESTING IN AN OPPORTUNITY ZONE

The PAE Living Building opportunity zone cash investors were eligible for three key tax advantages, per the Tax Cuts and Jobs Act of 2017:

1. Temporary deferral of taxes on previously earned capital gains. Investors can place existing assets with accumulated capital gains into opportunity funds. Those existing capital gains are not taxed until the end of 2026 or when the asset is disposed of.

2. Basis step-up of previously earned capital gains invested. For capital gains placed in opportunity funds for at least 5 years, investors' basis on the original investment increases by 10 percent. If invested for at least 7 years, investors' basis on the original investment increases by 15 percent.

3. Permanent exclusion of taxable income on new gains. For investments held for at least 10 years, investors pay no taxes on any capital gains produced through their investment in Opportunity Funds (the investment vehicle that invests in opportunity zones).*

* www.taxpolicycenter.org/briefing-book/what-are-opportunity-zones-and-how-do-they-work#:~:text=Temporary%20deferral%20of%20taxes%20on,the%20asset%20is%20disposed%20of.

"On the office side of things, companies have been dealing with green building for a long time but in retail, it's just never really been a factor. So this was a unique and exciting opportunity for us as retail brokers. I can't think of any other project where we had these parameters to work with."

BROCK SWITZER
HSM Pacific

"We do have to talk about the Living Building Challenge with all tenants, lenders, and landlords, just like what was done at the Bullitt Center. But once we get into the discussion, people quickly realize what they need to do to adhere to the goals and requirements of the Challenge."

NATHAN SASAKI
Apex Real Estate Partners

NET OPERATING INCOME

Being the first structure of its kind, the PAE Living Building had no financial precedent on which to base any assumptions about how the project would perform.

Still, there are two basic variables in any pro forma that determine a commercial property's return on cost (net operating income divided by total project cost): 1) development costs (including land, design, construction, and financing costs) and 2) rental income from tenants (a function of rentable square footage and rent per square foot), allowing for a 5 percent average vacancy rate. Looking longer term, the internal rate of return looks at equity invested and cash received back over time in the form of annual cash flow and the profit generated by an assumed sale of the asset at some point in the future.

To achieve the PAE Living Building's targeted 10 percent rate of return over a ten-year period,* the project would need a reliable source of rental income.

ANCHOR OFFICE TENANT: PAE — FLOORS 3-5
As the tenant with its name on the building, PAE committed to renting the top three floors. Plus, the firm had agreed early on to pay a 10 percent premium on its lease (relative to typical Class A Portland rents) as a way of helping the project pencil out. They had done something similar in Seattle for the space they rented in the Bullitt Center, only to find that market rates quickly passed the "elevated" rent they had agreed to in their initial lease. So, within a few years of moving into their first Living Building offices, PAE was enjoying a discount of approximately 20 percent relative to Class A Seattle market rates. Prior to COVID-19, PAE expected the same market dynamics to play out in Portland, although the pandemic slowed down this process.

TENANTS SUB-LEASING PAE SPACE — FLOOR 4
PAE sub-leased portions of its space to like-minded organizations. Edlen & Co. was first to commit to a fourth-floor sub-lease. Soon after, two non-profit organizations did the same: the New Buildings Institute (which pushes for better energy performance and lower carbon emissions in the built environment) and Earth Advantage (which advances knowledge to the trades and consumers to accelerate the building industry's adoption of sustainable practices).

REMAINING OFFICE TENANTS — FLOOR 2
Nathan Sasaki at Apex Real Estate Partners, who also helped secure PAE's initial and expansion leases in the Bullitt Center, began the search for second-floor PAE Living Building tenants while the project was still under construction. The layout was adaptable, so he approached some early prospects about leasing the entire second floor as well as others that would only lease half or a quarter of the space. He quoted these spaces at market rate, targeting prospective tenants who would be drawn to the productivity benefits and potential marketing advantages of operating out of a Living Building. When the building opened its doors, half of the second floor was in lease negotiations with Beneficial State Bank, a financial institution committed to social justice and environmental benefits whose Seattle branch is located in the Bullitt Center.

*The project's targeted 10 year IRR was 10 percent. However, at the commencement of construction, the actual underwritten IRR was 8.3 percent.

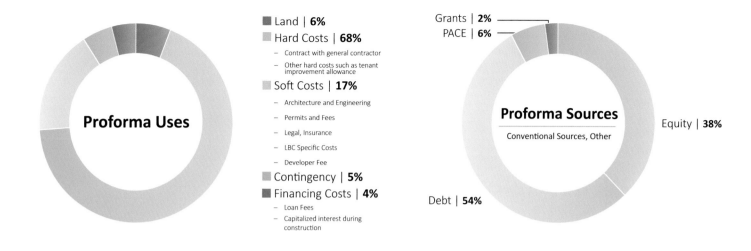

Proforma Uses
- ■ Land | **6%**
- ▨ Hard Costs | **68%**
  - – Contract with general contractor
  - – Other hard costs such as tenant improvement allowance
- ▨ Soft Costs | **17%**
  - – Architecture and Engineering
  - – Permits and Fees
  - – Legal, Insurance
  - – LBC Specific Costs
  - – Developer Fee
- ▨ Contingency | **5%**
- ■ Financing Costs | **4%**
  - – Loan Fees
  - – Capitalized interest during construction

Proforma Sources
Conventional Sources, Other
- Grants | **2%**
- PACE | **6%**
- Equity | **38%**
- Debt | **54%**

Although there are cost premiums associated with constructing a Living Building, the overall split of costs in the PAE Living Building were similar to what would be found in any traditional commercial building. The design fees as a percentage of construction costs are higher on Living Buildings to account for the extra design associated with net zero energy, net zero water, and material research, as well as costs associated with achieving other Imperatives in the Living Building Challenge.

RETAIL TENANTS — GROUND FLOOR

Brock Switzer at HSM Pacific was responsible for leasing the street-level retail spaces. He began his search by targeting select local and national retailers recognized for their environmental missions, knowing there would be buzz about this first-of-its-kind Portland opportunity. Food service tenants were not an option due to their high energy and water usage, but most other categories were on the table. When shopping the spaces, Switzer quoted rents at market rate. Efforts to lease the building's ground-floor spaces were slowed by the COVID-19 pandemic, which dramatically affected the retail environment in Portland, as was true in most major cities. In addition, many street-level businesses in downtown Portland were boarded up in 2020, either temporarily or permanently, due to protests and social unrest, which further hindered the process of securing retail tenants for the PAE Living Building. It was expected that by late 2021, when the office tenants were moving into the building's upper floors, opportunities to rent the ground level would open up.

WRITING THE CHALLENGE INTO LEASES

All PAE Living Building tenants need to understand, embrace, and adhere to the Living Building Challenge. That starts with making sure everybody grasps the fundamentals of the Challenge. It also means that certain language is written into each lease to ensure that occupant behavior supports the building's operational performance goals. For example, office and retail tenants are required to limit energy use. (As an engineering company with significant computing needs, PAE would normally have higher energy use than typical office tenants but the firm has spent considerable time reducing its loads and now shares those ideas with its fellow PAE Living Building tenants to support them in their energy conservation efforts.) In addition, there are Red List-specific requirements spelled out in the leases that relate to certain tenant improvement efforts.

THE PAE LIVING BUILDING: *Developer-Led, Nature-Inspired*

HOW DID WE DO IT?

- Equity by Designers, Developer, and Contractor
- Opportunity Zone
- Reasonable Investor Return
- Anchor Tenant
- Low Interest Rates

PAE LIVING BUILDING: CHANGE IMPACTS ON INTERNAL RATE OF RETURN

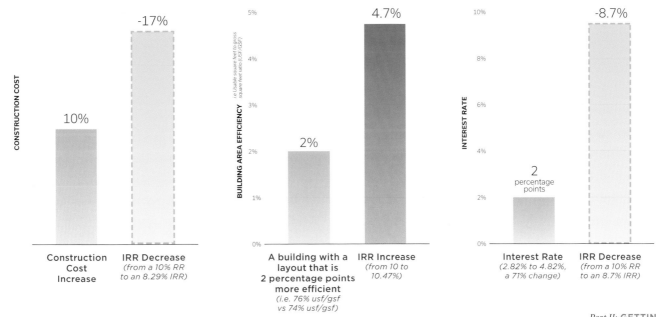

CONSTRUCTION COST

10% — Construction Cost Increase

-17% — IRR Decrease *(from a 10% RR to an 8.29% IRR)*

BUILDING AREA EFFICIENCY *(i.e. Usable square feet to gross square feet ratio (USF/GSF)*

2% — A building with a layout that is 2 percentage points more efficient *(i.e. 76% usf/gsf vs 74% usf/gsf)*

4.7% — IRR Increase *(from 10 to 10.47%)*

INTEREST RATE

2 percentage points — Interest Rate *(2.82% to 4.82%, a 71% change)*

-8.7% — IRR Decrease *(from a 10% RR to an 8.7% IRR)*

33

"Everything was starting to shut down just as we were about to break ground on the building. So the timing on that made us wonder, after all of this effort we'd spent designing the building, would we now have a big delay because of COVID. But the WALSH team did a fantastic job working through all of that and keeping us on track."

PAUL SCHWER
PAE

"That spring, we had no idea where the pandemic was going; there was so much uncertainty. But it was one of these things where we just had to be committed to this thing and do the best that we could. We decided we'd just lock arms and figure out what to do as we went. It took a lot of flexibility and effort by a lot of people to keep it moving forward."

ED SLOOP
WALSH

THE ROLE OF 2020

It is critically important to remember that construction for the PAE Living Building began in spring 2020, a pivotal season in a year like no other. There were numerous unpredictable and unprecedented things happening in the background that threatened the success — and even the survivability — of this project.

A GLOBAL PANDEMIC

Workers broke ground on the PAE Living Building on April 1, 2020, mere weeks into the COVID-19 pandemic that brought previously normal business and social activities to an abrupt stop in Portland and around the world. Oregon's Governor Kate Brown declared a state of emergency on March 8 followed by bans on gatherings of more than 250 people (on March 12) and more than 25 people (on March 17). On March 23, she issued a statewide stay-at-home order. Although the order included provisions that allowed most construction projects to continue, the constantly changing state of restrictions called into question which, if any, members of the PAE Living Building's construction team would even be allowed to show up to the site.

WALSH quickly assembled what they called their COVID SWAT team, meeting every day to revise protocols to help keep workers safe in the office and on job sites. It actually benefited the PAE building to be so early in its construction phase as these new systems were being defined. For one, the on-site team needed to adhere to the protocols nearly from the beginning of the project,

which normalized the processes. Also, it was still an open, airy site, which helped leave plenty of space and fresh air between workers. Face masks, hand washing, and social distancing quickly became the norm on the site and adapting to COVID requirements did not end up slowing down the construction schedule.

PROTESTS AND SOCIAL UNREST

Even as the pandemic was taking hold, people around the country held demonstrations, marches, and protests related to racial injustice and police brutality, largely triggered by the killings of George Floyd, Breonna Taylor, Ahmaud Arbery, and numerous other Black Americans. In Portland, these activities began in late May and continued nearly daily for months. The majority of the gatherings were peaceful, but some began to get heated enough to involve confrontations with both counter-protesters and law enforcement. By June, many downtown storefronts were boarded up; by August, at least one person had died in protest-related violence. Images of the 2020 Portland riots became iconic.

"Russ Brotnov's house burned to the ground at a critical time for the project, but he and everyone at Carpentry Plus never missed a beat. They were an A-plus partner."

ED SLOOP
WALSH

Work continued on the project (including construction of the building's core, shown here) even as Portland's skies filled with smoke during the 2020 fire season.

Many who marched for these causes walked into downtown Portland via the Burnside Bridge, just two blocks north of the PAE Living Building. So having streams of people passing the construction site became the norm. For members of the project's stakeholder group, this raised important questions about equity. Had they, as privileged owners and future occupants of a Living Building, done enough to minimize the kinds of disparities that the protesters were shining light on? Beyond meeting the Living Building Challenge Equity Petal Imperatives, what else could the project do to benefit its community?

More than a year earlier, the team had come up with a plan to locate a supplemental off-site solar array at a partnering affordable housing development (Renaissance Commons in Portland's Kenton neighborhood). While they were initially quite disappointed that the PAE Living Building would not be able to achieve energy independence on-site, the team eventually grew to recognize that the off-site array, which would also

provide valuable electricity to Renaissance Commons, served both energy and equity goals for the project. The 2020 protests helped reinforce the importance of this community-minded strategy. (For more on this story, see the Energy and Equity Petal chapters.)

WILDFIRES

The heat raging in and around Portland in the summer of 2020 was figurative and literal. According to Oregon's Department of Forestry, the fire season began that year on July 5. By the end of the season, more than a million acres had burned statewide, more than 4,000 homes were destroyed, and at least seven people died as a result of wildfires.* Fires got close enough to metropolitan Portland to require several people associated with the PAE Living Building project to evacuate their homes. Russ Brotnov, owner of Carpentry Plus, which assembled the project's mass timber frame, lost his own home to fire just days before framing was set to begin. Still, Russ and his team kept the project on track and on schedule.

* www.en.wikipedia.org/wiki/2020_Oregon_wildfires

GETTING THE CITY'S BLESSING

Living Buildings are meant to effect change and upend outdated ways of adding to the built environment. As such, few municipal codes have been amended to accommodate the types of systems usually seen in Living structures. So the process of seeking and securing permits can be ... challenging ... for projects that are serving as local pioneers.

Once the PAE Living Building's design concept was essentially set, the core team scheduled a meeting with the City of Portland to discuss the plans. They assumed they would meet with a handful of city representatives. Instead, they walked into a room filled with approximately 30 people from virtually every key department that would potentially have any say in approving the project.

As is often the case when city officials are reviewing plans for aspirational Living Buildings, Portland's permitting bodies were very open to the idea but unfamiliar with most of the concepts being presented. Additionally, to get comfortable approving the plans, they needed help to understand how the different performance areas were tied to and dependent upon each another. To be fair, this was only the second Living Building ever attempted in the city limits, so these officials were just getting up to speed. (The first was the June Key Delta Community Center in the Albina district, which registered as an aspirational Living Building in 2009 and was still on a path to ILFI certification as of 2021.) So the PAE Living Building project team, which had been deep in a collaborative process for more than a year at that point, had to remember that the people on the other side of the table had not. It was the team's job to convince the city officials of the wisdom of integrated solutions — whether designing or permitting a new building.

In the end, the city's permitting process took approximately nine months from start to finish. There were a few hiccups along the way, several appeals, and a handful of accommodations made. There were meetings with the mayor and more with members of the city council. (Also of note: the PAE Living Building was one of the first projects to go through the city's paperless permitting system. This meant navigating some uncharted territory on both sides, but it proved to be a time-, money-, and tree-saving process that the project team was happy to help launch.) Finally, the project secured its permit approval on April 1, 2020, which cleared the path forward for Portland's first Living Building project. It was officially time to take on the Petals.

PART III

Coming to Life

Petals, Imperatives, and Performance

Part III: **COMING TO LIFE**

Looking eastward over Waterfront Park, the Willamette River, and Portland's Eastside, with Mt. Hood visible in the distance.

THE PAE LIVING BUILDING: *Developer-Led, Nature-Inspired*

HOW THE LIVING BUILDING CHALLENGE WORKS

The Living Building Challenge is comprised of seven performance categories, or "Petals": Place, Water, Energy, Health + Happiness, Materials, Equity, and Beauty. Petals are subdivided into a total of twenty Imperatives, each of which focuses on a specific sphere of influence.

There are two rules to becoming a Living Building:

- All Imperatives are mandatory. Many of the Imperatives have temporary exceptions to acknowledge current market limitations.

- Living Building Challenge certification is based on actual, rather than modeled or anticipated, performance. Therefore, projects must be operational for at least twelve consecutive months prior to evaluation for the majority of the Imperatives' verification. Some Imperatives can be verified after construction, through a preliminary audit.

The PAE Living Building registered under version 3.1 of the Living Building Challenge. The following chapters explore the ways in which the project team approached each Petal and all associated Imperatives.

NOTE: Portions of this book were researched and written while the PAE Living Building was under construction and it went to press prior to full occupancy. The book has been produced under the assumption that the project would eventually achieve certified Living Building status after completing its initial twelve-month operational phase and formal performance audit by the International Living Future Institute.

THE PLACE PETAL

Here and Now

The Place Petal: **HERE AND NOW**

THE PLACE PETAL
LIVING BUILDING
CHALLENGE VERSION 3.1

PETAL INTENT
The intent of the Place Petal is to realign how people understand and relate to the natural environment that sustains us. The human built environment must reconnect with the deep story of place and the unique characteristics found in every community so that story can be honored, protected, and enhanced. The Place Petal clearly articulates where it is acceptable for people to build, how to protect and restore a place once it has been developed, and how to encourage the creation of communities that are once again based on the pedestrian rather than the automobile. In turn, these communities need to be supported by a web of local and regional agriculture, since no truly sustainable community can rely on globally sourced food production.

The continued spread of sprawl development and the vastly increasing number of global megapolises threatens the few wild places that remain. The decentralized nature of our communities impedes our capacity to feed ourselves in a sustainable way and also increases transportation impacts and pollution. The overly dense urban centers, in turn, crowd out healthy natural systems, isolating culture from a sense of place. As prime land for construction diminishes, more development tends to occur in sensitive areas that are easily harmed or destroyed. Invasive species threaten ecosystems which are already weakened by the constant pressure of existing human developments. Automobiles, often used as single-occupancy vehicles, have become integral to our communities when we should depend on "people power" — walking and bicycling — as the primary mode of travel, and supplement it with shared transit.

PETAL IMPERATIVES
• Limits To Growth
• Urban Agriculture
• Habitat Exchange
• Human Powered Living

ON THIS SITE

~10,000 BC – 1800s
NATIVE LAND FOR NUMEROUS
NORTHWEST TRIBES

1883 – mid-1900s
THE REID'S
BLOCK BUILDING

mid-1900s – 2020
SURFACE
PARKING LOT

2021
PAE LIVING BUILDING

HONORING THOSE WHO CAME BEFORE

Long before the arrival of Meriwether Lewis and William Clark, or pioneer settlers, or the timber industry, or *Portlandia*, or PAE itself, the land on which the PAE Living Building now stands was home to Indigenous people. For many thousands of years, the area now known as metropolitan Portland was abundant enough to serve approximately 200,000 members of a variety of tribes, including the Multnomah, Wasco, Cowlitz, Kathlamet, Clackamas, bands of Chinook, Tualatin, Kalapuya, Molalla, Atfalati, the Confederated Tribes of Grand Ronde, and more.* Thanks in large part to the bounty of the Columbia and Willamette rivers, the region provided ample natural resources to sustain these Native American communities year after year, generation after generation.

* www.up.edu/disclosures/land-acknowledgment.html
and www.native-land.ca

Lewis and Clark reached the Pacific Coast in 1805. Then, beginning in the mid-1800s, European settlers laid claim to more than 2.5 million acres of the Oregon Territory in the span of only seven years.* Although Multnomah County was named to honor a band of Chinooks when it was founded in 1854, the local tribes reaped few benefits in the wake of the settlers' arrival. Oregon went on to become a state in 1859.

When Portland was incorporated in 1851, it had a population of only 800 non-native residents. It took just 50 years for Portland's population to reach 100,000 (about half the size of the population of Native Americans who had lived in the entire region for thousands of years). The PAE Living

Building seeks to pay tribute to its region's original inhabitants by honoring and protecting the natural environment they held in such high regard.

Artist Toma Villa, a member of the Yakama Nation who grew up in Portland, was commissioned to create the striking wood carving that stands in the lobby of the PAE Living Building. The piece celebrates the winds that blow through the Columbia River Gorge — honoring both the ancient Native traditions surrounding these powerful winds as well as their modern role in renewable energy. (For more on this artwork, see the photo on page 23 and additional information in the Beauty Petal chapter.)

* www.travelportland.com/culture/native-american

"The Eurocentric settlement of the Pacific Northwest brought tremendous changes to a cultural and natural landscape that was in place for hundreds of times longer than cities like Portland have existed. Unfortunately, the sum of these changes has led to serious environmental and social problems that urgently need to be addressed. We sincerely hope that the PAE Living Building and other similar projects will help lead a sharp pivot from our previous and still current destructive path to one that is much more equitable, sustainable, and regenerative for all people and the natural environment."

MARC BRUNE
PAE

HISTORIC SKIDMORE/ OLD TOWN

The Portland neighborhood known as Skidmore/Old Town is roughly bounded by the Willamette River to the east, SW Harvey Milk Street to the south, SW 3rd Avenue to the west, and NW Davis Street to the north.* Home to some of the oldest buildings in Oregon, Skidmore/Old Town was Portland's first recognized historic district, earning a spot on the National Register of Historic Places in 1975 and designated as a National Historic Landmark in 1977.

When first developed, the area was rich with cast-iron buildings that housed companies and agents supporting the city's robust 19th-century trade industry.

The three-story Reid's Block building was erected in 1883 at the corner of SW 1st Avenue and SW Pine Street where the PAE Living Building now stands. Historic records show that for some period of time, the Portland National Bank occupied the ground floor of Reid's Block's while the German Remedy Company, an addiction treatment center, occupied the two upper floors.

Sometime in the mid-1900s, the Reid's Block was torn down and replaced by a surface parking lot eventually owned by the Downtown Development Group. That lot remained on the site for approximately seventy years — nearly half of Portland's named existence.

* www.portlandmaps.com/detail/zoning-district/Portland-Skidmore-Old-Town-Historic-District-NHL-/SO_did

47

LANDING AT SW 1ST AVENUE AND SW PINE STREET

PAE began searching for a site in February 2017 in a process that was surprisingly short and sweet.

"I assumed we would end up walking a lot of sites to scope out locations and land. I also assumed that we'd end up on the Eastside, just for affordability, but we didn't even end up looking at Eastside options. It turns out, the Eastside is already more expensive than some sites on the Westside. Once we saw this corner, it was pretty clear pretty quickly that it would check all the boxes. So the site selection went much faster than I thought it would."

PAUL SCHWER

Nathan Sasaki of Apex Real Estate, an investor in the project, prepared a map of metropolitan Portland that showed all prospective building sites whose cost could potentially align with the early financial parameters for the project. Sasaki reviewed the map with PAE's Paul Schwer, Scott Bevan, and Nick Collins, as the group planned its multi-site tour. However, a certain corner in Skidmore/Old Town stood out as the best potential combination of location, cost, and zoning, so they went there first. As it turned out, they did not need to look elsewhere. They had found the most promising future home for the PAE Living Building.

The corner of SW 1st Avenue and SW Pine Street was ideal for a number of reasons:

SOLAR ACCESS

Being in a historic neighborhood meant that there were height restrictions on all surrounding buildings. The site was deep enough into Skidmore/Old Town that nothing within two blocks to the south would ever be allowed to rise higher than 75 feet, so shade would not threaten the PAE Living Building's ability to harvest sunlight on its rooftop photovoltaic (PV) array or rely on daylight to bathe interior spaces.

PRICE

The height restrictions in the district also made the land less expensive than sites where developers were free to build much taller structures with more rentable space. The team estimated that a comparably sized piece of land located only four blocks to the south (just outside the limits of Skidmore/Old Town) would have cost three or four times more. In addition, the fact that the site only allowed for 58,000 square feet of development made it so that the PAE lease would represent a significant percentage of the building. This meant a building on this site would be mostly pre-leased, helping to further reduce risk.

CONVENIENCE

The site was mere blocks from PAE's then-headquarters (in the Yeon Building, built in 1911 and located at SW 5th Avenue and SW Alder Street), keeping it in close proximity to the vast majority of the firm's clients, downtown amenities, and public transportation. It was also only a block from the expansive Waterfront Park and within easy walking and biking distance of Portland's bustling Eastside (accessible via the Burnside Bridge, three blocks to the north and the Morrison Bridge, three blocks to the south).

The MAX Light Rail makes its way along the historic cobblestones of SW 1st Avenue, passing directly in front of the PAE Living Building (visible on the right).

A DDG PROPERTY

The Downtown Development Group (DDG) owned the parking lot that stood on the site, which proved to be advantageous for several reasons. To begin with, DDG Co-President Greg Goodman had a longstanding personal and professional history with Mark Edlen, co-founder of Edlen & Co., so he trusted the project's integrity and mission from the start. Secondly, Goodman and DDG (a four-generation family-run Portland operation) opted to invest in the project and offered to hold the property until the financing closed, allowing the ownership group to avoid taking out a loan, buying the site, and carrying interest expenses as they did their due diligence. DDG's involvement helped connect some of the final pieces in the project's pro forma.

"We'd previously been to visit the Bullitt Center in Seattle, so once we heard about the idea for this project, we quickly came to understand. We didn't create the vision for this building, so our role isn't equal to what the designers and engineers did. But we had the dirt so we're almost like caretakers of the land. If somebody had come to us and said they wanted to build a warehouse there, we would have said no, regardless of what they were willing to pay. The PAE Living Building project set a very high bar and we were really happy to participate."

GREG GOODMAN
Downtown Development Group

STUDYING THE ARCHITECTURAL HISTORY

As part of their pre-design research, the ZGF Architects design team did a deep dive into the proportions of the historic buildings that have stood on or near the site that the PAE Living Building would later occupy.

They sought ways to translate similar glazing, opening, and pattern rhythm details into the look of the new project. Interestingly, the original 19th- and early-20th-century Skidmore/Old Town buildings tended to have very tall first floors and moderately tall upper floors, as the higher windows helped drive daylight farther into the interiors when electric lighting was unavailable and/or in short supply. Other elements of the historic district, such as operable windows, shallow floor plates,

shorter buildings, and small urban blocks, also helped achieve the project's sustainability goals.

The result is a PAE Living Building that echoes — but doesn't copy — its Italianate architectural precedents. Design details are updated, as are certain material choices and most construction processes. Still, the project pays subtle, beautiful tribute to those that came before it. (For more on this topic, see the Beauty Petal chapter.)

The Skidmore/Old Town neighborhood is rich with design influences.

THE DECKONY

Here's a riddle: What do you get when you combine the expanse and fresh air of a rooftop deck with the indoor/outdoor feel of a balcony? The answer, of course, is a deckony.

This perfectly apt mash-up word began as a riff in a design meeting, when ZGF's Kathy Berg spontaneously offered it up to describe the building feature they were sketching. The term amused the team, and from that point forward, it just stuck ... so much so that it ended up in the permit documents, cementing its place in the PAE Living Building lexicon.

The deckony occupies approximately 1,500 square feet of the southeast corner of the building's fifth floor. It is among the many project features that satisfy more than one Living Building Challenge Imperative. In the context of the Place Petal, it helps celebrate the natural beauty of the precise location where the structure stands.

AN EXTERNALLY CONNECTED INTERIOR

Officially, the deckony is PAE's "break room." It was designed to serve as an inviting and welcoming gathering area that blurs the line between inside and outside spaces.

AN ALTERNATIVE TO A ROOFTOP DECK

In any building powered by PV panels, top-of-the-building real estate is precious. That fact, combined with district height restrictions that prevented elevating the array any higher, meant that a rooftop deck was not an option for the PAE Living Building. The deckony brings all the same benefits down one floor, freeing the rooftop space for the PVs, rainwater collection, mechanical equipment, and fire department access. Plus, the deckony provides rain protection in inclement weather, so it can accommodate indoor or outdoor uses.

"We spent a lot of time on the site trying to think about the connectivity that it had to the broader Northwest landscape, the waterfront, and the river. We even flew a drone at one point to try to get an understanding of what you would see from each floor as you went up into the building. All of that came into play when we were designing the deckony."

KATHY BERG
ZGF Architects

"The deckony was actually on the value-engineering chopping block and didn't initially make it into the bid documents because of the price of the windows. But we all really wanted it. Once Ed Sloop had finalized the costs of some of the larger components, he felt comfortable adding this feature back in by using his construction contingency. We appreciate Jill Sherman allowing WALSH to carry a construction contingency (in addition to the developer contingency that Edlen & Co. carried) because it helped make the deckony possible. It's a wonderful part of this building."

PAUL SCHWER
PAE

A DISAPPEARING WALL OF WINDOWS

The windows on both the south- and east-facing walls of the deckony fold away accordion-style to create a completely open-air corner of the building on the fifth floor. Constructed using a manually-operable NanaWall aluminum frame system with full-height glass and no horizontal mullions, the design opens up that section of the building envelope from about two feet above the floor all the way to the ceiling. (See photos on pages 102 and 105.)

A RIM OF PLANTERS

The deckony is framed by a perimeter of planter boxes the tops of which reach to a height of 38 inches to keep the space safe while enhancing its biophilic beauty. The planters also provide an opportunity for urban agriculture (an Imperative of the Place Petal). Green-thumbed PAE employees can take breaks from work to tend to that season's planter bounty.

A MAGNIFICENT VISTA

The deckony offers views of the Willamette River and Mount Hood (especially visible in the less leafy winter months), as well as glimpses of the street-level goings-on in the neighborhood below. The architects worked hard to orient the space to capture the best of what the site and its visible surrounding landscape have to offer.

A HISTORICALLY RESPECTFUL DESIGN

The deckony's design helps echo the base-middle-top vocabulary found elsewhere in the historic architecture of Skidmore/Old Town. The PAE Living Building's ground floor presents the taller program, with the three middle floors of office space filling in the central section of the façade. Situating the deckony, with its distinct recessed window wall element, on the most visible upper corner of the structure allowed the designers to create another level of architectural articulation that caps the building and ties it to its historic context. It also helped to get the blessing of the Historic Landmarks Commission.

IMPERATIVE:
HUMAN POWERED LIVING

This Imperative of the Living Building Challenge calls for each project to "contribute toward the creation of walkable, pedestrian-oriented communities" and to "enhance the ability of a community to support a human powered lifestyle." The PAE Living Building meets these goals with ease, via:

99 WALK SCORE®. The site boasts nearly the highest possible Walk Score rating, qualifying as a "walker's paradise" by the company that ranks neighborhood walkability.

STEPS FROM THE LIGHT RAIL. Both the Red and Blue Lines of the MAX Light Rail run along SW 1st Avenue, just steps from the building.

BLOCKS FROM TWO BRIDGES. Commuters coming from Portland's Eastside can use either the Burnside or Morrison Bridge, both of which accommodate pedestrians and cyclists.

ON-SITE BIKE STORAGE. A 40-stall bike storage room is tucked into the northeast corner of the building's ground floor.

ON-SITE SHOWERS. All tenants have access to ground-floor showers, which facilitates walking, running, and cycling commutes.

NO ON-SITE VEHICLE PARKING. The building does not include vehicle parking within its footprint.

STROLLING THROUGH THE SUBJECT OF SIDEWALKS

When the Skidmore/Old Town neighborhood first sprouted in the 19th century, there were few (if any) sidewalks along SW 1st Avenue. The street, which was still made of dirt (and possibly covered in boards), was continuous from building face to building face. It was also narrower than modern city streets because it only needed to accommodate horses, buggies, and pedestrians. When nine-foot sidewalks were eventually added, it further shrank the street's width, as did the addition of the MAX Light Rail line in 1986.

City of Portland codes evolved to meet the changing needs of pedestrians, cyclists, and other forms of non-vehicle transportation. Municipal sidewalk width requirements have expanded from nine to twelve to a full fifteen feet in some locations around the city. When the PAE Living Building project team was mapping out the building's footprint, they needed to satisfy several agencies. The Department of Transportation wanted to maximize sidewalk width while the Historic Landmarks Commission preferred that the building face be held tight to the property line (which meant the sidewalks would remain at nine feet rather than be increased to current city standards) to match the neighborhood's original style. Meanwhile, the Urban Forestry Commission advocated for wider sidewalks as a way of preserving as many street trees as possible.

Many months were devoted to balancing each department's interests with the design, performance, environmental, and financial goals of the project. (A wider sidewalk would reduce the building's rentable square footage; the more trees that had to be removed, the more intense the need to find an elegant and environmentally-friendly way to repurpose them; etcetera.)

In the end, all parties were satisfied. The PAE Living Building footprint extends to its full width to maximize rentable space. The sidewalks along the SW 1st Avenue side of the building are nine feet wide with window and door insets at the building base to allow additional width for pedestrian traffic, while sidewalks along Pine Street are twelve feet wide. Street-level planters add a biophilic character and enhance the sidewalk landscape. Finally, the red maples that once stood along the SW 1st Avenue thoroughfare were transformed into beautiful new furniture and cabinetry for PAE's reception area and new trees were planted to replace them. (For more on this furniture story, see the Beauty Petal chapter.)

"There were a lot of gymnastics around the sidewalk issue. There were conversations about pedestrians and trees and rentable square footage. At one point, we even explored setting back the building on the ground floor and then cantilevering it back out on the upper floors. But the pro forma needed that rentable space on every floor, so that's what we worked hard to get."

ED SLOOP
WALSH

"If you go back to an old Italian village, you're still meandering through the streets on pathways that haven't really changed, so the cars and the people overlap. In this case, we were required to create the separation of all the different modes like you would in a modern street, but we're doing it in a street that was originally scaled for a whole different purpose."

KATHY BERG
ZGF Architects

RIGHT UP PAE'S ALLEY

The PAE Living Building's location helps support its primary tenant's very culture.

The firm has always actively encouraged "walking meetings" whenever possible as a way to create a healthy, collaborative dynamic for one-on-one and small-group conversations. Now, the leafy, grassy 1.5-mile ribbon of Waterfront Park is only a block away from PAE's Portland office, making riverside walking meetings even more accessible. Alternatively, bridge routes offer one- to three-mile loops from the building's front door to the Eastside and back.

Waterfront Park also serves as an expansive "front yard" for the PAE Living Building. Within moments, tenants can go from office space to open space, where they can kick soccer balls, play bocce ball, toss Frisbees, or simply sit in nature. In a poetic tie to the project, Waterfront Park first sprouted in the 1970s after U.S. Route 99W was removed from that north-south stretch along the Willamette. The same Greg Baldwin who urged PAE Founder Pete Peterson to stay in Portland back in 1967 and later became a ZGF Architects partner was instrumental in working with the city to remove the highway and create Waterfront Park. The urban greenspace now supports a variety of flora and fauna and is a popular public amenity in the heart of downtown.

The Place Petal: **HERE AND NOW**

THE WATER PETAL

Drop by Drop

The Water Petal: **DROP BY DROP**

THE WATER PETAL
LIVING BUILDING
CHALLENGE VERSION 3.1

PETAL INTENT

The intent of the Water Petal is to realign how people use water and to redefine "waste" in the built environment so that water is respected as a precious resource.

Scarcity of potable water is quickly becoming a serious issue as many countries around the world face severe shortages and compromised water quality. Even regions that have avoided the majority of these problems to date due to a historical presence of abundant fresh water are at risk: the impacts of climate change, highly unsustainable water use patterns, and the continued drawdown of major aquifers portend significant problems ahead.

PETAL IMPERATIVE

• Net Positive Water

THE PAE LIVING BUILDING: *Developer-Led, Nature-Inspired*

Portland's Skidmore/Old Town historic district sits directly adjacent to the Willamette River.

WORKING WITH A WATERY SITE

The first step in mapping out the PAE Living Building's water strategy was factoring in the realities and restrictions of the project's location. There were two primary challenges right off the bat:

SITE CONDITIONS. Given the building's proximity to the Willamette River, the water table is very high. Additionally, tight soils and potential contamination on-site made an infiltration strategy virtually impossible.

A COMBINED SEWER SYSTEM. The building is in a combined sewer area of downtown Portland. This means that both stormwater and sewage end up in the same pipe once they leave the building. It also means that any treated greywater and blackwater leaving the building would end up in the same municipal pipe as stormwater.

61

The Water Petal: **DROP BY DROP**

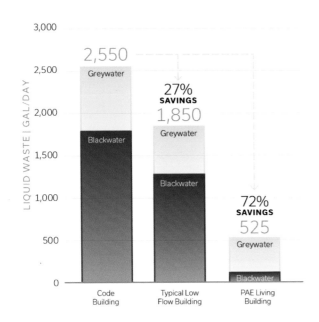

8,000 gal. of urine per year are processed to create liquid and powdered fertilizer.

Estimated market value of liquid fertilizer is approx.

$50,000
PER YEAR

Estimated market value of 400 lbs powdered fertilizer equal to less than

$500
PER YEAR

A SIMPLY ELEGANT SOLUTION

Just as forests and fields do, the PAE Living Building gathers its water from the sky before returning it to the watershed.

Rainwater that falls on the roof journeys through drains, pipes, tanks, treatment systems, pumps, and fixtures to meet all of the building's water needs. Even greywater is captured, treated, and reused. Any excess ultimately makes its way out of the structure. Given downtown Portland's 43 inches* of average rainfall each year, nature delivers the necessary bounty to keep the building's functions and occupants suitably hydrated.

Here are the keys to that process:

RAINWATER IS CAPTURED. All rain that falls on the 11,000 square foot roof, including the precipitation that runs off the photovoltaic panels, flows to one of three drains placed on the slightly graded rooftop. (The entire rooftop surface is covered with a thermoplastic polyolefin [TPO] roofing membrane that is approved for potable water collection by NSF International.

* www.wrh.noaa.gov/pqr/pdxclimate/pg89.pdf

For more on this story, see the Materials Petal chapter.) Rainwater is then channeled from the roof through the building core toward the cistern beneath the building's ground floor.

ON-SITE CISTERN SERVES AS STORAGE. While Portland's total annual rainfall is enough to serve the building, very little of it falls in the summer months, which is why significant on-site storage is required. When rain does fall, it first moves through a pre-filter station before continuing on to a 71,000 gallon cistern located beneath the building's lobby and extending all the way to the northwest corner of the property. The team calculated 37 years of daily Portland rainfall data (from 1980 to 2017) to determine the cistern's size and capacity to ensure that there would be sufficient on-site inventory between rain events even in drought years. When the cistern reaches capacity, excess stormwater is diverted to the municipal sewer since it cannot be infiltrated on-site.

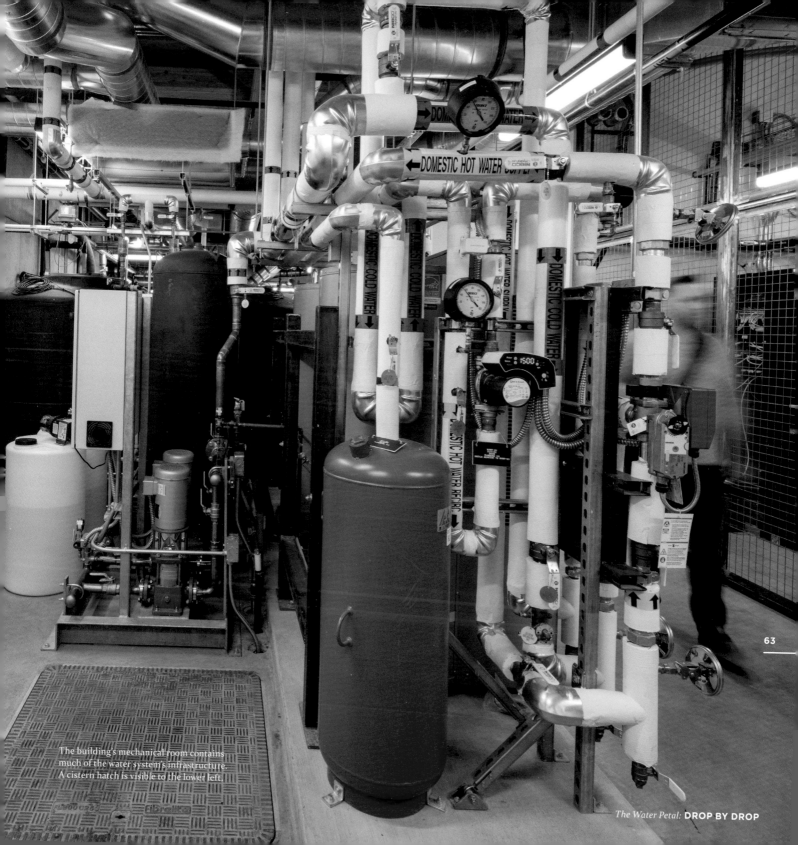

The building's mechanical room contains much of the water system's infrastructure. A cistern hatch is visible to the lower left.

63

The Water Petal: DROP BY DROP

Twenty composting bins are situated on the ground floor, collecting waste from toilets located throughout the building.

THE PAE LIVING BUILDING: *Developer-Led, Nature-Inspired*

NET ZERO WATER
100% OF WATER COMES FROM ON-SITE RAINWATER

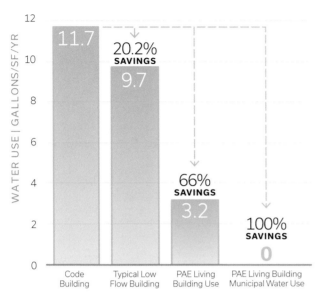

WATER USE | GALLONS/SF/YR

- Code Building: 11.7
- Typical Low Flow Building: 9.7 — **20.2% SAVINGS**
- PAE Living Building Use: 3.2 — **66% SAVINGS**
- PAE Living Building Municipal Water Use: 0 — **100% SAVINGS**

73%
BETTER THAN CODE

100%
**LESS MUNICIPAL
WATER USE SAVINGS**

"The cistern got redesigned a few times because we were trying to find the right size and shape that would make it constructable while finding a Red List-compliant waterproofing system and also keeping it cost-effective. We ended up wrapping it around the shear core in a manner that didn't require shoring and reduced surface area of concrete and excavation versus other configurations while also being (dimensionally) highly constructable. To me, that all ties into the water story because we needed to balance these innovative systems with the construction and cost challenges that came with them."

ED SLOOP
WALSH

WATER IS TREATED FOR POTABILITY. To be classified as potable, water is pumped from the cistern through a treatment system with microfiltration, ultraviolet (UV) light, and carbon filtration before being disinfected by chlorine. Interestingly, as of version 3.1 of the Living Building Challenge, chlorine treatment was written into the Water Petal as an exception to facilitate on-site rainwater treatment solutions that adhered to state water codes and Environmental Protection Agency (EPA) regulations. This was one of the many lessons learned from the Bullitt Center. (See the "Learning from the Bullitt Center" section of this chapter for more.)

POTABLE WATER IS DELIVERED TO FIXTURES.
After water is treated to potable standards, it flows through hot and cold water pipes leading to sinks and lavatories throughout the building's five floors and to showers on the ground floor.

GREYWATER DRAINS BACK DOWNSTAIRS. Once the potable water has been used, it flows back to the building's ground floor to a greywater storage tank and treatment system. Treated greywater is transformed into a non-potable water supply used to flush vacuum toilets and urinals on every floor. (Although the urinals are referred to as "waterless," they flush

approximately once per day to rinse the collection lines and fixtures.) Since the site has too high a water table to infiltrate all wastewater on-site, greywater not used for irrigation or flushing gets pumped to the municipal sewer. ILFI granted an exception for this.

BLACKWATER GETS DIVIDED. Water leaving toilets and urinals is channeled through separate dedicated drain lines. Liquid waste from urinals flows into a 1,000 gallon nutrient recovery tank. Water from toilets carries waste to one of 20 composting bins located on the first floor. Leachate generated from the compost bins is collected in a 2,000 gallon collection tank.

EXCESS WATER EXITS VIA THE MUNICIPAL SYSTEM.
When the PAE Living Building opened its doors, the small amount of excess water that left the building drained to a single municipal pipe because a combined stormwater/sewer system was the only option available in downtown Portland. Nonetheless, all discharge is treated to a high level before it leaves the site. Plus, the team future-proofed the building by including both a storm pipe and a waste pipe leading from the site to accommodate potential upgrades that might later be made to the city infrastructure.

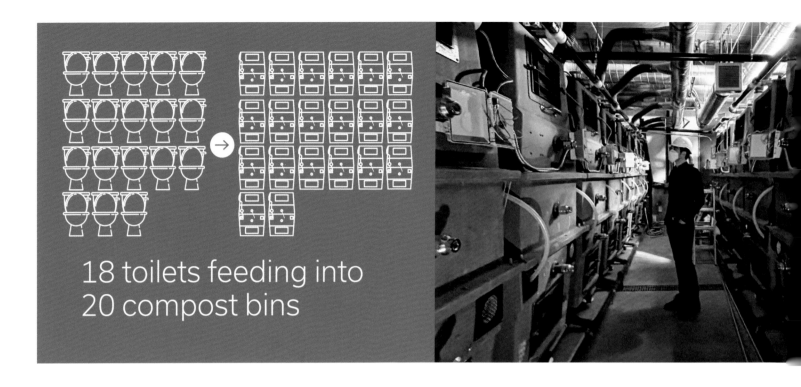

18 toilets feeding into
20 compost bins

RESTROOM FIXTURES
WORTH BRAGGING ABOUT

The PAE Living Building hosts a first-of-its-kind multistory toilet infrastructure that serves more than one of the project's performance areas.

Eighteen "vacuum on demand" (VOD) flush toilets are distributed around the building, all connected to ground-floor composters. Somewhat similar to fixtures found on airplanes (but quieter), the toilets use vacuum power rather than swirling water to extract waste. Whenever one of the toilets gets flushed, an automated system determines which composter should receive the contents to ensure that waste is distributed equally among all of the composters.

The toilets are manufactured by Jets Vacuum AS in Norway with an adjustable flush flow rate that only requires between one- and three-tenths of a gallon per flush — between 81 and 94 percent less than traditional toilets. (Traditional modern toilets typically use

about 1.6 gallons per flush, while older fixtures can use as much as seven gallons per flush.*) The vacuum piping is also more flexible in terms of sloping than standard plumbing, which created a wider range of space planning options for the building's designers.

Both liquid and solid waste travel from the vacuum-flush toilets to the composters. The building also has 14 waterless urinals, which divert approximately 9,400 gallons of urine annually to a dedicated urine tank for nutrient recovery.

*   www.watercalculator.org/posts/toilet

HVAC System for Radiant Floor Heating and Cooling

IT and MDF Room

Batteries and UPS for Emergency Power

BESS (Battery Energy Storage Systems) for Microgrid and Resiliency

Switchgear, Transformer, Microgrid Energy Control Center

Rainwater to Potable Water Treatment and Hot Water Heating

Greywater Treatment

Nutrient Recovery Treatment: Urine conversion to liquid and powder fertilizer

Blackwater Treatment: Composters

GROUND FLOOR

67

The Water Petal: **DROP BY DROP**

> *"Most fertilizer production right now is heavily fossil fuel-based and trucked all over the country. The fact that this building is creating a local fertilizer is pretty amazing and adds a whole different dimension to decarbonizing our communities."*

PETE MUÑOZ
Biohabitats

WATER CYCLE

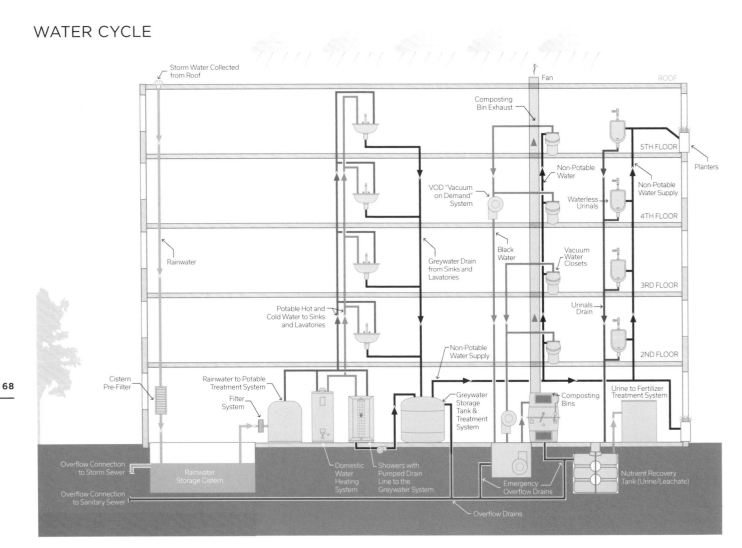

Storm Water Collected from Roof

Fan

ROOF

Composting Bin Exhaust

5TH FLOOR

Non-Potable Water

Non-Potable Water Supply

Planters

VOD "Vacuum on Demand" System

Waterless Urinals

4TH FLOOR

Rainwater

Black Water

Vacuum Water Closets

Greywater Drain from Sinks and Lavatories

3RD FLOOR

Urinals Drain

Potable Hot and Cold Water to Sinks and Lavatories

Non-Potable Water Supply

2ND FLOOR

Cistern Pre-Filter

Rainwater to Potable Treatment System

Greywater Storage Tank & Treatment System

Composting Bins

Urine to Fertilizer Treatment System

Filter System

Overflow Connection to Storm Sewer

Rainwater Storage Cistern

Domestic Water Heating System

Showers with Pumped Drain Line to the Greywater System

Emergency Overflow Drains

Nutrient Recovery Tank (Urine/Leachate)

Overflow Connection to Sanitary Sewer

Overflow Drains

THE BENEFITS OF "WASTE"

Not even waste is wasted at the PAE Living Building. All liquid and solid waste gets treated on-site via one of two systems that turn blackwater into rich sources of nutrients, making this the first office building in North America to produce fertilizer on-site from captured waste.

COMPOSTING BINS. Twenty composters stand side-by-side on the ground floor ready to receive waste from the building's vacuum-flush toilets. Each composter receives a "dose" pumped from the flush collection tank and then the valve closes and material is sent to the next composter in the line. As a result, material is evenly distributed among all of the composters rather than having specific toilets deliver waste to specific composters and filling the composters unevenly. (There is also one extra valve incorporated into the composting infrastructure that can send waste directly to the municipal sanitary lines if the on-site system ever malfunctions.) Urine separation helps minimize the moisture in the composters, enhances the system's performance, and helped reduce the number of required composters from 24 to 20. The composters' solid contents are manually stirred on a regular basis. When the cycle is complete after approximately one year, the finished product — a Class B biosolid — may be removed and used for beneficial land application in accordance with regulations of the Oregon Department of Environmental Quality (DEQ). Liquid from the composters is collected in an underground leachate storage tank. Leachate is periodically pumped out by truck and can be applied at agronomic loading rates for beneficial off-site re-use.

URINE-TO-FERTILIZER TREATMENT. An estimated 9,400 gallons of urine per year is collected and processed into fertilizer. Urine is pumped from the nutrient recovery tank through a stainless steel distillation column, where generated steam strips the nitrogen for recovery. The fertilizer manufacturing equipment includes heat exchangers to help make the process as efficient as possible. Magnesium is added to precipitate out phosphorus. Once the nutrients have been recovered from urine, all that remains is salty water, which is discharged to the municipal sewer system. The recovered nutrients create two products: a powdered phosphorus-rich fertilizer (struvite) and a liquid ammonia bicarbonate (a nutrient-rich solution with a pH level of approximately 12, which is ideal for hydroponic growing). Each product is a retail grade fertilizer and will be registered with the Oregon Department of Agriculture.

FERTILIZER RESALE VALUE. On an annual basis, the fertilizer produced on-site at the PAE Living Building has a resale value of approximately $50,000, so it can be used as an ongoing source of revenue for the ownership group.

SERVING THE CARBON MISSION. The on-site composting process and fertilizer production is a powerful way for the PAE Living Building to meet its operational carbon goals. This process of using rainwater and urine to capture nutrients, composting, producing fertilizer, and distributing it locally for agricultural use also helps demonstrate what is possible with regard to decarbonizing urban communities and creating a circular economy where there is no longer any "waste."

> "The timing on the lessons learned from the Bullitt Center was really critical to this project. The overlapping engineering team also helped, as we were so familiar with the operational details on the Bullitt Center. That ended up being really important to how we approached the design at the PAE Living Building."

CONRAD BROWN
PAE

> "The main thing that sets this building's water strategy apart from what was originally done at the Bullitt Center — or is being done anywhere else — is that we're producing retail grade fertilizer from the urine stream on-site. That's quite a differentiator; this is the only building I know of that's doing that."

PETE MUÑOZ
Biohabitats

LEARNING FROM THE BULLITT CENTER

Seattle's Bullitt Center informed and inspired many elements of the PAE Living Building. In the context of the Water Petal, it proved to be a bold and valuable forerunner.

Since PAE was involved in helping craft the Bullitt Center's water strategies, the firm was very familiar with the system's intricacies. Plus, PAE has been a tenant in the Bullitt Center since it opened in 2013, so they were able to gather seven years of first-hand experience before even breaking ground on their own Living Building.

One of the most profound lessons learned relates to toilets. Originally, the Bullitt Center installed foam-flush toilets that were revolutionary in their minimal water and energy use while also adhering to the Water Petal Imperatives of Living Building Challenge 2.1, under which the project was registered. (More recent versions of the Challenge allow a broader range of wastewater treatment options than those written into version 2.1.) While the Bullitt Center's foam-flush fixtures helped raise the profile of composting toilets and served as a proof of concept for other urban projects considering similar systems, they ended up not being the best solution for that particular site, building type, or desired user experience.

In 2020, with the approval of the International Living Future Institute (which will not alter the building's Living status), the Bullitt Center replaced its foam-flush toilets with vacuum-flush alternatives. The decision helped validate the PAE Living Building's team choice to use a vacuum-flush system in their own headquarters.

Bullitt Foundation CEO Denis Hayes eloquently addressed the change by saying, "The Bullitt Center is a giant science experiment. We integrated lots of bleeding-edge technologies. If everything had worked perfectly, that might have meant we hadn't been bold enough."

70

The Bullitt Center, a 52,000 square foot commercial Living Building in Seattle, opened its doors in 2013.

The Water Petal: **DROP BY DROP**

A MULTIPRONGED PERMITTING PROCESS

Securing permits for Living Buildings' water systems always involves a variety of agencies due to their complex and, in most cases, unprecedented designs.

For the PAE Living Building, traditional plumbing infrastructure permits needed to come from the City of Portland, potable water systems required Oregon Health Authority (OHA) approval, and on-site treatment strategies had to be blessed by the state DEQ.

Although the building's overall water strategy would be the first of its kind in Portland, it was important that it be replicable to honor one of the project's underlying goals. So, on the plumbing side, the team worked hard not to stray too far from standard approaches. Still, since the plumbing tied to the system's other more complicated water elements, the city was not quick to grant approvals. That's when the team planned a road trip. In summer 2019, PAE's Conrad Brown and Luke Hendricks led a one-day up-and-back between Portland and Seattle to guide city plumbing inspectors through a tour of the Bullitt Center. It was an opportunity to show how a comparable system operates in real time; an actual rather than a theoretical demonstration.

The team also held what they called a "water regulatory summit" in Portland, inviting all jurisdictions associated with water — from the city, county, and state — to come together and weigh in with questions or concerns related to the project's plans. The team, too, posed questions of their own about necessary permitting requirements and exceptions given the project's new and different approaches.

The Bullitt Center visit, the regulatory summit, and ongoing open communication with inspectors all helped enormously, as the permitting bodies did finally grant approval for the PAE Living Building's water infrastructure. The OHA issued its water supply permit in December 2020 and the DEQ approved the wastewater strategy (including greywater, composting, and nutrient recovery systems) in April 2021.

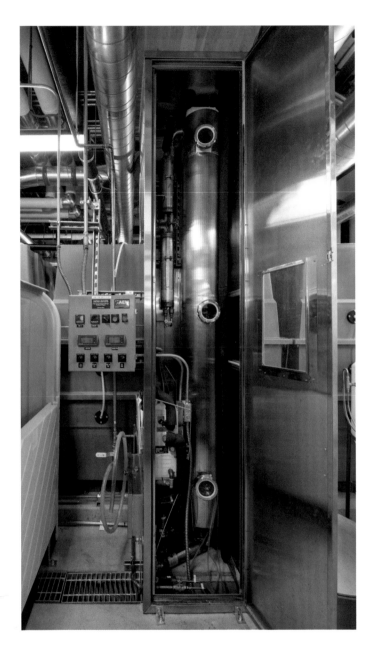

"We always wanted to make this a replicable building. We didn't try to get a ton of exceptions from the code or from the city permits when it came to water; we didn't want to blaze a trail. It was important for the city and other project teams to be able to use the same design."

LUKE HENDRICKS
PAE

EXPLORING THE IDEA OF CONVERTING BLACKWATER TO POTABLE WATER

On their way to crafting what became the final design for the PAE Living Building's water strategy, the team pondered adding a residential component to the building.

But when they calculated what it would take to meet the associated water budget, they determined that the only way to balance things out would be to convert some of the on-site blackwater to potable water. They quickly concluded that this approach would be too complicated and would be better suited to an eco-district or municipal scale effort rather than a single structure. More importantly, it would not be an easily replicable system, which went against one of the project's fundamental missions.

THE ENERGY PETAL

The Power of Innovation

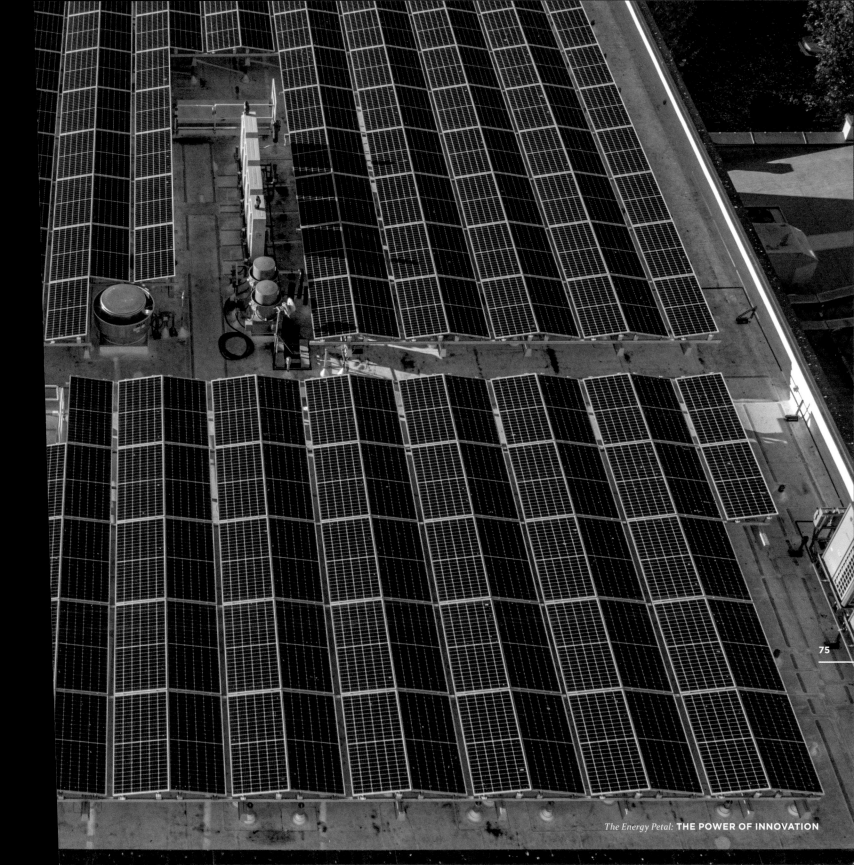

The Energy Petal: **THE POWER OF INNOVATION**

THE ENERGY PETAL
LIVING BUILDING CHALLENGE VERSION 3.1

PETAL INTENT

The intent of the Energy Petal is to signal a new age of design, wherein the built environment relies solely on renewable forms of energy and operates year round in a safe, pollution-free manner. In addition, it aims to prioritize reductions and optimization before technological solutions are applied to eliminate wasteful spending — of energy, resources, and dollars. The majority of energy generated today is from highly polluting and often politically destabilizing sources including coal, gas, oil, and nuclear power. Large-scale hydro, while inherently cleaner, results in widespread damage to ecosystems. Burning wood, trash, or pellets releases particulates and carbon dioxide (CO_2) into the atmosphere and often strains local supplies of sustainably harvested biomass while robbing the soil of much-needed nutrient recycling. The effects of these energy sources on regional and planetary health are becoming increasingly evident through climate change, the most worrisome major global trend attributed to human activity.

PETAL IMPERATIVE

• Net Positive Energy

INITIAL ATTEMPTS TO KEEP PVS ON-SITE

Relying on renewables for on-site power is one of the most common strategies for any project that is considered even remotely green. And achieving net positive energy is the one and only Imperative written into the Living Building Challenge Energy Petal. Members of the PAE Living Building team came into the project having designed numerous net zero and net positive energy systems on many other buildings over the years, both individually and collaboratively.

So when it came time to consider how best to achieve net positive energy for the PAE Living Building, the team turned first to on-site photovoltaic (PV) panels. It helped, too, that some of the project's core energy strategists had previously worked on Seattle's Bullitt Center, another commercial Living Building on a tight urban site that relies on rooftop solar — and, in the case of the Bullitt Center, an expansive set of sidewalk overhangs — for its energy needs.

77

The team sketched out several options in an attempt to keep enough PV panels on-site to generate the ~368,000 kWh per year the PAE Living Building would need. This would be equivalent to an Energy Use Intensity (EUI) rating of 19.5 plus an additional 5 percent allowance to be net positive. In addition to using whatever rooftop space was not already being used by other required components, the team looked into these possible supplemental strategies:

WEST-FACING VERTICAL ARRAY. PV panels could be affixed to the upper two floors' façades on the building's west face. This would capture the exposed walls not butting up against the adjacent Pine Street Market.

NEIGHBORING ROOFTOP ARRAY. Additional panels could be placed on the next-door roof of the Pine Street Market if a suitable contract could be struck with that organization.

ROOFTOP CANOPIES. PV-covered canopies could be suspended over all other rooftop elements (walkways, mechanical equipment, the rainwater capture system, etcetera), essentially capturing 100 percent of the rooftop square footage.

PHOTOVOLTAIC SPANDREL. Glass with PV properties could be used for the building envelope to help the exterior walls serve the energy mission.

SIDEWALK OVERHANGS. PV panels could be suspended from the roofline to extend out and over two of the sidewalks below, similar to what was done in dramatic fashion at the Bullitt Center. (This concept was quickly dismissed due to City of Portland historic district restrictions, which do not allow PVs to be visible from the street level.)

The more the team explored these options, the less promising they seemed. The ideas may have succeeded in reaching target energy numbers, but they failed to hit more important targets: They conflicted with the project's design intents; they threatened neighboring structures' solar access and visibility rights; they failed to honor the neighborhood's historic flavor; they were inefficient; they were expensive. The team quickly realized that simply making the energy numbers pencil out was not enough. What mattered more was creating a Living Building that kept Energy in proper balance among all the seven Petals of the Challenge.

An early ZGF sketch from 2018 reveals the fixed limit
for on-site energy production by square foot of area,
ultimately leading the team to explore off-site solutions
for energy generation and sharing of energy resources.

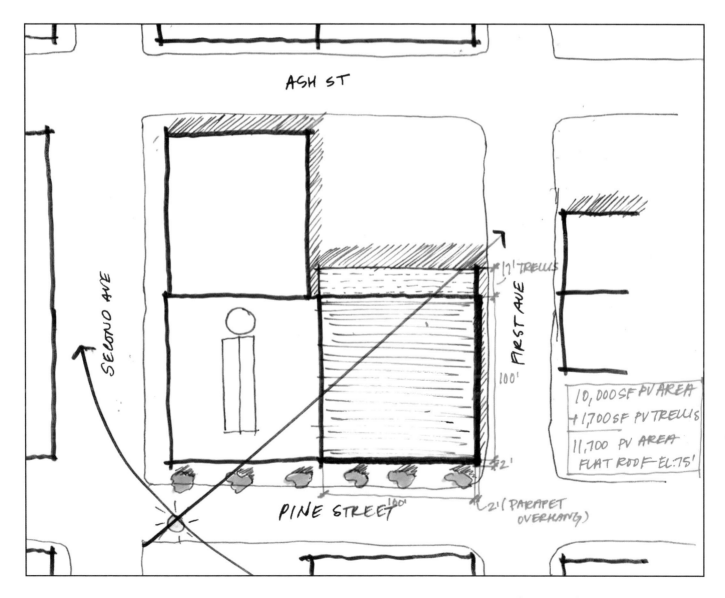

ASH ST

SECONO AVE

FIRST AVE

↑ 7' TRELLIS

100'

2'

2' (PARAPET
OVERHANG)

PINE STREET 100'

10,000 SF PV AREA
+ 1,700 SF PV TRELLIS
11,700 PV AREA
FLAT ROOF EL: 75'

The Energy Petal: **THE POWER OF INNOVATION**

"We started the design process off with a 'We're PAE; we don't need certification exceptions and we aren't afraid of challenging old codes' type of attitude. We were determined to get the approvals to put all the PV on the building, because we thought if we didn't then we would have failed. But then we looked at the big picture and realized we needed to redefine what failure with these systems really meant."

KARINA HERSHBERG
PAE

"The types of grid limitations that we faced in Portland are pretty common in dense urban settings. But from a resiliency standpoint and a sustainability standpoint, this is a regulatory and engineering hurdle that has to be overcome. It was important to us to work closely with the regulatory groups and utilities to try to overcome that hurdle, because when we did, it opened up an opportunity for on-site resiliency and sustainability."

GRANT PARTHEMER
PAE

GRID CONSTRAINTS

The team faced another serious obstacle as it explored ways to keep solar on-site: the configuration of the downtown Portland electrical grid, which is designed to protect the neighborhood's access to power but makes it extremely difficult for any single building to "backfeed."

Such a configuration, and the limitation it poses, is common in urban settings. The ten-to-twelve blocks surrounding the PAE Living Building are all served by a single network within the grid, with multiple utility feeders flowing into that network. The transformers are interconnected in a N+1 fashion, so the loss of a single transformer or feeder does not necessarily interrupt the electrical service. While this arrangement supports the utility's resilience, it caps the amount of PV-generated power that any individual building can backfeed to the network because excessive backfeed could potentially darken several downtown blocks at one time by lightening the network load and unbalancing the network protection. (This would cause the transformers to be taken off-line automatically.)

PAE appealed directly to Portland General Electric (PGE), explaining that while the project would have its own controllable microgrid with battery energy storage, the net positive energy goal would require some amount of backfeed to the electrical grid and net energy metering. The team was determined to show PGE that it would be possible to construct a fully energy-independent building in a historic district and that if any project could successfully blend the old and the new, it would be this one. It would also enable the building to be a "utility-friendly" net positive energy building.

Although theoretically possible under certain conditions, net metering with intentional power flow to the network has never been achieved in Portland's downtown network. As with all new endeavors, there were unknowns and risks to overcome. Still, as a progressive utility company, PGE was interested in accommodating the types of advanced approaches that the PAE Living Building would represent. However, there was no precedent for such a thing so PGE outlined the requirements for an interconnected system based on the technical and regulatory limits of the local infrastructure. Details included a maximum backfeed limit of 54kW (which was reduced to 49kW in 2020 due to COVID-related demand reductions on the area network). The PAE Living Building team then set off to figure out how to meet those requirements.

THINKING OUTSIDE THE (FOOTPRINT) BOX

Once it was clear that the building would not be able to generate all of its own energy on-site, it was time to rethink the energy strategy. Just as virtually every Living Building project team that came before them had to do, the PAE Living Building team needed to think creatively, considering approaches that may never have been attempted before. By looking at the problem from a different angle, they landed on a clever solution that ended up meeting more than one Living Building Challenge Imperative.

As it turned out, it was just a matter of stepping back and looking at the bigger picture; being open to the kinds of nested solutions that are typical of Living Buildings.

During a strategy session in which various project goals were being discussed, Ed Sloop from Walsh Construction Co. mentioned that his company was simultaneously building Renaissance Commons, an affordable housing project in north Portland. Was there a way to address both projects' energy needs while also supporting a worthy community development resource?

Sloop got in touch with his contact at REACH Community Development, the developer of Renaissance Commons, who helped connect Edlen & Co.'s Jill Sherman with her counterpart at REACH. Eventually, a plan emerged: The team would install 215 kW of PV on the roof of Renaissance Commons' primary structure to supplement the 133 kW of on-site PV at the PAE Living Building.

Since PGE serves both properties, both locations' PV arrays would deliver energy to the same regional grid. In combination, the two systems would generate sufficient energy to power Renaissance Commons' common areas and about 5 percent more electricity than what the PAE Living Building would need annually.

This energy "donation" translates to approximately $20,000 in funds that REACH Community Development would otherwise be paying annually for Renaissance Commons' electric bills and can now devote to other services that benefit their residents directly. In addition to this ongoing support and the donation of the ~$600,000 of PV infrastructure, the PAE Living Building ownership group made a $90,000 cash donation to REACH to deepen its commitment to the organization and further tie the project's energy and equity missions. (Equitable Investment is one of the Equity Petal's four Imperatives.)

An east-west "accordion" configuration prevents "self-shading" and allows more PV panels to fit on the roof.

AN UNDULATING ROOFTOP

The collection of PV arrays that now sits on the PAE Living Building's roof is configured in alternating waves of east- and west-facing panels. While many PV panels installed in the Northern Hemisphere face south, this east-west "accordion" arrangement on the PAE Living Building captures sunlight during both morning and afternoon hours. It also allows for a greater number of panels per unit area, as they are placed directly adjacent to one another rather than being spaced out to avoid self-shading while all oriented in the same southerly direction. The panels all sit at a 10 degree slope, which permits sunlight to reach them as soon as it rises past the building's parapets.

THE BRAINS OF THE BUILDING

Although the PAE Living Building's PV rooftop array does not generate enough annual energy to power the entire building, it delivers energy to another very important component of the project: the on-site battery. A 120 kW (280 kWh) lithium-ion battery sits in an electrical room on the ground floor and is constantly responding to the ebb and flow of the building's power and energy needs.

The battery's size, which is twice what the Living Building Challenge would require for this project, was determined by calculating the maximum summertime production on a sunny weekend day when the building would be mostly unoccupied and figuring out how much energy the unit would need to store. After pulling in all the energy that can be generated on such a day by the 133 kW rooftop PV array, it slowly releases that energy back to the grid — always careful to stay below PGE's 49 kW net metering limitation. The next day, the battery repeats the same cycle. Over the course of a year, this give-and-take microgrid system allows the building to achieve net positive energy (with the supplemental help of the off-site array at Renaissance Commons).

The microgrid also keeps an intelligent eye on the building and its power patterns. It monitors the PVs' generation, all the electrical loads throughout the structure, the PGE grid, and the building's own microgrid. Using those data points, the battery can either charge, discharge, curtail loads, or even turn off loads and switch to emergency operation mode if necessary.

The Living Building Challenge requires that any on-site battery must retain power equivalent to 10 percent of the building's lighting load for one week. This battery far exceeds that capacity. Using only a few energy-saving strategies (such as keeping lights turned off during the day and adjusting temperature setpoints), the PAE Living Building could operate in low energy mode completely off-grid during the summer months for approximately 100 days using only the energy generated each day by the on-site PV and the energy stored in its battery. This will allow the building to be "invisible" to the grid should the utility ever need to curtail power during a heat wave or a wildfire, both of which are becoming more common.

The building's powerful lithium-ion battery system allows the building to operate completely independent of the power grid when needed.

The Energy Petal: **THE POWER OF INNOVATION**

An engineer from Schneider Electric tests the building's microgrid control center.

PGE PLUGS IN

Just as was true when the PAE Living Building team navigated the water permitting process, securing approvals for the project's proposed energy strategy meant introducing the local utility company to approaches that had never before been tried.

In fact, the team quickly discovered that the very documentation they were asked to fill out to begin the process did not allow for much variation beyond traditional energy infrastructure designs. There was literally no box they could check on the forms they needed to submit that would come close to describing the energy system they were planning.

Again, just as was true with water, they decided to take the show on the road. PAE's Paul Schwer, Grant Parthemer, and Karina Hershberg arranged to meet in person with a room full of PGE representatives to explain the big-picture intent of the Living Building Challenge as well as the particulars of the PAE Living Building's energy vision. It was critical that they helped these utility officials understand both the Challenge and the renewable energy solution. They wanted to shine light on how the building would interact with the downtown core grid and inspire PGE to get excited about collaborating on this game-changing approach.

The exercise was successful. The utility began to understand not only what this one project wanted to do, but also all the ways its innovative strategies might help usher in a new energy future for Portland. From that point forward, the PAE Living Building team has collaborated closely with PGE, studying the limitations of the local network and mapping out requirements that would allow interconnection of this building without jeopardizing service to neighboring structures. Indeed, once the permitting process was complete, PGE was pleased to have the PAE Living Building serve as a sort of test case that will give the utility an opportunity to observe how the project's microgrid functions with the electrical grid.

"Nobody goes to work thinking, 'I really hope I make no difference in the world today.' Everybody wants to go to work and do something cool. But utilities rarely see the details of the buildings they serve so we had to help PGE see how cool this building would be. We did that by setting aside the paperwork and meeting personally with them to show them what was possible and how we could work together to make it happen. That's when they started to say, 'Yes. Let's do this.' You're never going to make that kind of change with paperwork; you've got to do it with people."

KARINA HERSHBERG
PAE

87

LETTING IN THE SUNSHINE

An obvious way to reduce a building's energy usage — specifically, its need for electric lighting — is to maximize the amount of natural sunlight that can enter interior spaces. A structure's orientation, window height, and position relative to neighboring buildings all factor into this equation. The PAE Living Building site did not offer flexibility when it came to orientation or neighbors, so the team had to rely on design to address daylighting.

They began with several atrium variations that would wrap the building around an open core to allow daylight to stream in from both sides of the occupied spaces. But no atrium would be big enough to supply the necessary light to reach the energy goal while also preserving enough rentable square footage inside the building to suit the pro forma. The designers also sketched out numerous core configurations, looking for the best spot where the building's elevator shaft, restrooms, and other essential (but artificially lit) elements could be situated without blocking natural daylight.

The final daylighting strategy accounts for each side of the building:

WEST. The Pine Street Market, a two-and-a-half-story historic structure, sits next door to the west. The first three western-facing floors of the PAE Living Building have no windows, but the fourth and fifth floors feature tall windows that allow abundant afternoon light to enter. Given the historic classification of the Pine Street Market, it is unlikely to be altered any time in the near future.

NORTH. When the PAE Living Building opened its doors in 2021, an undeveloped parking lot sat directly to the north. So the building's original iteration incorporated plenty of glazing on the north face via a mix of operable and inoperable windows. However, if a building is erected on the adjacent lot in the future, it will undoubtedly affect the amount of daylight that enters that side of the PAE Living Building. (The ownership group has an agreement with the City of Portland that states that the north-facing windows will be filled in if the adjacent lot gets developed all the way to the lot line so that fire ratings may be met on both buildings.)

SOUTH AND EAST. The two "open" sides of the PAE Living Building feature generous glazing from ground floor to roofline, supplying substantial natural light into the building's interior via a design that honors downtown Portland's historic past. (Interestingly, these two façades are made up of only 30 percent glazing, but the visual impression suggests far more.) The street-level spaces are relatively shallow, which makes it easier for daylight to reach deep into their most highly trafficked areas. To drive the daylight deeper into the space, the perimeter beams on the south (as well as the north) are upturned and placed above instead of below the floor, with the floor itself hanging from the beam rather than sitting on it. This allows the windows to go all the way up to the cross-laminated timber (CLT) ceiling and provides more space for the daylighting to penetrate the interior.

88

The Energy Petal: **THE POWER OF INNOVATION**

THE PAE LIVING BUILDING: *Developer-Led, Nature-Inspired*

"The design approach on this project is one of the most nuanced in my career. Mechanical systems are often complex, large, and dominate the space planning. For the PAE Living Building project, we had optimized so many building elements for high performance that the HVAC design became, in part, an exercise in subtraction. We were constantly evaluating how to edit design elements to the essentials without compromising occupant experience. With all the exposed system elements throughout, everything required intentional placement while at the same time, not over-constraining the design and creating burdensome limits to future flexibility. And all of this, of course, was underpinned by the need to live within our energy, water, and capital budgets."

KATIE ZABROCKI
PAE

CREATURE COMFORTS

The PAE Living Building naturally takes care of its occupants.

HEATING AND COOLING. When considering heating and cooling, the team took full advantage of ever-improving heat pump technologies. When the Bullitt Center was built in 2011-2012, 26 bores were drilled 400 feet below street level to enable a ground-source geoexchange (geothermal) system. A decade later, the PAE Living Building relies on rooftop air source heat pumps that deliver nearly the same efficiency at a fraction of the construction and installation cost. The rooftop heat pumps serve a refrigerant-to-water variable refrigerant flow (VRF) "hydro-kit" that provides interior heat and cooling through the hydronic radiant floors. Conference rooms and other areas that need supplemental cooling are fed from fan coil units with DX coils connected to a separate rooftop air source heat pump system. Due to the building's inherent efficiencies, a rooftop system is sufficient to meet the building's thermal comfort needs without the need for any geothermal wells.

CEILING FANS AND RADIANT FLOORS. Occupant-controlled ceiling fans and a network of hydronic radiant piping that is embedded into the three-inch concrete floor slabs enhance comfort on all the office floors of the building (floors 2 through 5). The closed-loop radiant system circulates warm or cool water to modulate interior temperatures. The thermal mass of the flooring on the south-facing sections of the building also absorbs heat from the sun, which further supports the process of maintaining desired indoor temperatures.

SHADED, OPERABLE WINDOWS. Incorporating external window shades would have been more energy-efficient but were cost-prohibitive for the project. Instead, the building has internal shades throughout and all windows are either manually or automatically operable. In general, the higher windows are awning-style and mechanically controllable while the lower windows are casement-style and may be opened and closed by hand.

VENTILATION. The building's tall windows pay tribute to their historic predecessors in both form and function. In addition to echoing the aesthetics of the original Skidmore/Old Town neighborhood, the windows' height also supports the circulation of fresh air between the interior and exterior spaces. In addition to the natural ventilation system, each floor has a 100 percent dedicated outside air system (DOAS) that draws in outside air from the roof through a 72 percent efficient energy recovery ventilator (ERV). This recovers the energy from the air being exhausted from the space and transfers it to the outside air coming in (heating it in the winter and cooling it in the summer). This system provides approximately 30 percent more outside air than required by code and has the additional benefit of having no recirculated air. Plus, an optional "high flow" mode was added to the design in response to the COVID-19 pandemic, which will provide approximately 15 percent more air than originally designed and make full use of the system's fans.

> *"We took things to the next level with the PAE Living Building. Our core IT infrastructure (network and local servers) operates on the energy equivalent of one and a half hair dryers! We accomplished this while also improving both resiliency and performance in the bargain."*

SCOTT SCHUETZ
PAE

AN EFFORT TO UNPLUG

As is required in any Living Building, the PAE Living Building team drove down the energy use by optimizing anything that uses energy in the building. This strategy got the building down to an EUI of 19.5.

The biggest hurdle to overcome was plug loads, responsible for more energy use than anything in the typical office setting. Plug loads come from the devices that tenants bring into the building and plug in (computers, monitors, printers, etcetera). PAE is always working to significantly reduce plug loads. Instead of dual monitors, for example, PAE uses single high resolution widescreens that use less energy. Instead of printing, PAE marks up drawings digitally and has only one printer for more than 200 staff (and were on the way to becoming paperless by the time they moved into their Living Building). Instead of desktops, PAE shifted to 100 percent laptops in the late 2010s and then began to shift to a VDI (virtual desktop interface) that uses less energy than laptops. In addition, PAE had already moved more than 90 percent of their traditional IT infrastructure to the "green cloud" (servers, storage, email, backups, etcetera — all powered by renewable energy) prior to occupying their Living headquarters.

For the on-site services that needed to remain, PAE utilized special servers that run at approximately 10 percent of the energy required of a traditional server, which can drive down the building's EUI by nearly a full point. Also, PAE worked with some of the building's first tenants to develop a model by which PAE's equipment would power the tenants' IT infrastructure, eliminating the tenants' "base-loading" energy draws and reducing the building's overall usage.

ENERGY, CARBON, AND REFRIGERANT

While the Living Building Challenge addresses embodied carbon head-on in the Materials Petal, the spirit of the Challenge calls for reductions in both embodied and operational carbon throughout all Living Building performance areas.

In the context of the Energy Petal, the PAE Living Building minimizes its carbon footprint in two key ways:

MINIMAL REFRIGERANT. Known for their ozone-depleting and heat trapping characteristics, refrigerants have been identified as one of the biggest contributors to global warming. In fact, not long before the PAE Living Building came to be, the 2016 Kigali Amendment to the Montreal Protocol was announced, calling for a phase-down of hydrofluorocarbons (HFCs) due to their impact on global warming. The PAE Living Building minimizes the use of refrigerants by using refrigerant-to-water "hydro kits" and distributing most of the building's heating and cooling through water in the radiant heated and cooled slabs. Refrigerant piping does serve the conference room fan coils but the PAE Living Building uses substantially less refrigerant than buildings with full VRF systems. The very low energy use powered by renewable energy eliminates the structure's operational carbon and the very low refrigerant use reduces its refrigerant carbon profile.

DOUBLE-PANE WINDOWS. As part of its research into how to minimize energy use while maintaining interior comfort, the team looked into triple-pane windows — then quickly removed them from the plan. For one thing, they would not deliver enough energy efficiency in Portland's climate to justify their substantially higher price. Secondly, upon closer inspection, the team discovered that the extra embodied carbon of the triple-pane windows would not be offset by the reduced carbon emissions due to their increased efficiency over the life of the windows. So the PAE Living Building sports high-end double-pane windows with fiberglass frames that support its energy mission while lowering its carbon footprint.

A wall panel provides easy access to the radiant manifold, where zone-by-zone adjustments can be made to control the temperature of the floor slabs.

93

WELL AHEAD OF THE CURVE

In 2017, the City of Portland and Multnomah County announced a collaborative resolution to use renewables for 100 percent of community-wide energy needs by 2050. The commitment gave the city and county more than three decades to transition to clean energy. The PAE Living Building met this goal nearly 30 years ahead of schedule, proudly demonstrating to its neighbors in the Pacific Northwest and elsewhere that solar-powered structures — even in dense urban neighborhoods — are not only possible now but also can be powerful, profitable, community-minded pillars of the built environment.

The Energy Petal: THE POWER OF INNOVATION

THE HEALTH + HAPPINESS PETAL

Feeling Fine

The Health + Happiness Petal: **FEELING FINE**

THE HEALTH + HAPPINESS PETAL
LIVING BUILDING CHALLENGE VERSION 3.1

PETAL INTENT

The intent of the Health + Happiness Petal is to focus on the most important environmental conditions that must be present to create robust, healthy spaces, rather than to address all of the potential ways that an interior environment could be compromised.

Many developments provide substandard conditions for health and productivity, and human potential is greatly diminished in these places. By focusing attention on the major pathways of health, we create environments designed to optimize our well-being.

PETAL IMPERATIVES

• Civilized Environment
• Healthy Interior Environment
• Biophilic Environment

"Part of any company's recruitment and retention strategy is about having a space that's really special to work in. This building is an inherently special space that delivers so much to the people who work here that it saves us money by making it easier to recruit and retain staff."

PAUL SCHWER
PAE

TYING HEALTH TO PRODUCTIVITY

As a developer-led commercial venture, the PAE Living Building needs to be able to measure the various ways it can protect its investors' interests. The project team sought to prove at every turn that adhering to the world's most stringent green building standard can actually be replicable and profitable.

One way to quantify the benefits of the project in dollars and cents was to connect the dots between health and productivity using PAE, the anchor tenant, as an example.

The Health + Happiness Petal: **FEELING FINE**

> *"There are a lot of requirements in the Living Building Challenge, like net zero energy and water, that affect building performance but don't necessarily have any effect on productivity. They're probably good for recruiting and retention because they inspire employees, but they don't make you more effective in the building. The Health + Happiness Imperatives, however, are one of the keys to improved productivity."*

MARC BRUNE
PAE

Looking at the firm's operating costs, employee compensation and benefits account for about 75 percent of expenses, with rent responsible for only 5 percent. If working inside a Living Building leads to PAE's people being only about 1 percent more productive, the company would essentially break even after paying the 10 percent premium for its leased space. At 2 percent more productive, PAE would more than pay for the rent premium. (Studies have shown that daylit, biophilic workspaces can lead to productivity increases, helping to make the business case for such environments.*) In other words, operating out of a Living Building that supports the health and happiness of its occupants could potentially support the firm's fiscal resiliency while also providing a way to live its own mission.

*   www.workdesign.com/2018/09/enriching-
    the-workplace-with-biophilic-design

IMPERATIVE:
CIVILIZED ENVIRONMENT

This Imperative states, "Every regularly occupied space must have operable windows that provide access to fresh air and daylight."

The Materials Petal Handbook goes on to specify that staffed workstations must be located within 30 feet of operable windows. In a 58,000 square foot commercial office building that stands on a relatively small floor plate and comes with some significant perimeter impingements, meeting this goal proved quite challenging.

The PAE Living Building designers considered various shell and core layouts, arranging and rearranging the floor plate in ways that would situate all desks and other potential workstations within 30 feet of operable windows both for PAE and for other future tenants. They found it harder to achieve this Imperative than they originally expected because it affected numerous fenestration decisions. The biggest challenge was the lack of access to daylight on the first three floors of the west elevation, as the adjacent Pine Street Market sits on the property line and any future development on the north elevation might someday affect daylight. In addition, getting approval for windows on the property line from the building department was challenging and expensive, as it required providing rated windows on the north and west side and an easement agreement for the north windows.

Landing on the best solution meant locating the building's core in a way that maximized the amount of surrounding occupiable space near windows. In the end, the core was placed in the middle of the building where it allows for the best access to air and daylight (especially on the top two floors of the building).

Additionally, the designers put a lot of thought into how to create a sense of connection between the people inside and outside the building. This consideration was brought into sharper focus during the 2020 protests and riots in Portland, which coincided with construction. Those calls for social justice inspired the team to think about the people — both housed and unhoused — who live in the surrounding neighborhood and would regularly interact with the building, if even from the exterior. They wanted to avoid a sense of division between the occupants and the passersby and instead create a civil sense of connection. The generous glazing strategies help create this link between the activity and the movement happening on both sides of the building's walls.

A BREATH OF FRESH AIR

No recirculated air is pushed around the interior spaces of the PAE Living Building. Only fresh outside air flows through occupied areas via a combination of manually operable and automatic windows and through the 100 percent outside air heat recovery ventilators.

Since rooms are heated and cooled by radiant floors, the interiors remain comfortable over a much wider range of air temperatures than would be possible with a conventional office HVAC system. This allows the windows to remain open on more days of the year. Whatever the season, fresh air is always accessible.

To adhere to the precept of the Living Building Challenge, operable windows are within reach throughout all five floors. This feature gives occupants and visitors full control over both the ventilation and daylight allowed to enter the structure.

"Since the COVID pandemic forced people to get used to working from home, office spaces now have to be nice enough to lure people away from those comforts. So a civilized office place needs to be better than whatever setting people have in their own homes; we need to provide something special enough to draw people back into the office where they can collaborate in person."

PAUL SCHWER
PAE

IMPERATIVE:
BIOPHILIC ENVIRONMENT

Biophilic design abounds in the PAE Living Building. The architects wanted to reach well beyond additive biophilic elements; their goal was to integrate biophilia more profoundly so that people truly experienced it.

In its historic resource review document, ZGF Architects summarized the design's relationship to naturally occurring proportions in the statement below. (For more on the Fibonacci series, see the Beauty Petal chapter.)

"Analysis of the context has identified that many of the underlying proportional relationships of the [Skidmore/Old Town] district's architecture are rooted in the golden section, or Fibonacci series. It is of interest to the team that this proportional relationship is also applicable to many naturally occurring systems. There is an interesting interrelationship between these natural systems and our built environment particularly given the project's design as a Living Building. It is this intriguing collision of the natural and built environment, the historic context and contemporary rediscovery of passive design strategies rooted in optimizing the use of our natural resources that provide a basis and inspiration for the building's design development."

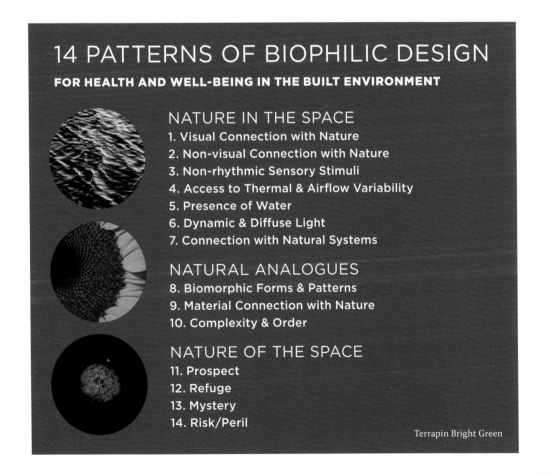

14 PATTERNS OF BIOPHILIC DESIGN
FOR HEALTH AND WELL-BEING IN THE BUILT ENVIRONMENT

NATURE IN THE SPACE
1. Visual Connection with Nature
2. Non-visual Connection with Nature
3. Non-rhythmic Sensory Stimuli
4. Access to Thermal & Airflow Variability
5. Presence of Water
6. Dynamic & Diffuse Light
7. Connection with Natural Systems

NATURAL ANALOGUES
8. Biomorphic Forms & Patterns
9. Material Connection with Nature
10. Complexity & Order

NATURE OF THE SPACE
11. Prospect
12. Refuge
13. Mystery
14. Risk/Peril

Terrapin Bright Green

"Creating a biophilic space is more than just putting in a green wall or adding something that looks like a literal tree. You have to think about a bigger, more structured, more integrated approach. That starts with proportions, but it also has to do with things like how light gets cast, how it moves, how it's dappled. I think that makes for more fulfilling architecture. And in a developer-led building, it's a timeless way to create spaces that will appeal to a range of lessees."

JUSTIN BROOKS
ZGF Architects

103

"Putting the deckony at the top of the building was an effort to provide a direct physical connection with nature by bringing the outside into the space. Being able to sit there with some protection and see out to the river, to the mountains, and beyond — that's a biophilic space; that's prospect and refuge."

JUSTIN BROOKS
ZGF Architects

"From the height of the deckony, your sense of scale within the city changes. That's what makes a good city: neighborhoods that have low-rise development so when you look out your window you still can see who's outside; you still have a sense of community."

MICHAEL O'MARA
ZGF Architects

"The deckony is just a fundamentally different space, not just for PAE but also for our neighbors in the Portland community. It's a true gathering place and I'm looking forward to seeing all the different ways it will be used. It really is the heart of the building."

NICK COLLINS
PAE

THE DECKONY: A FIFTH-FLOOR OASIS

Even before moving into its Living Building, PAE had operated using a "hoteling" office concept. With no assigned desks, employees are free to take their laptops and work wherever they'd like to be at any given time. Any available workstation, open conference room, or communal area will do.

The hoteling model honors individual preferences, adapts to changing workflow dynamics, promotes movement, and — key to the Living Building Challenge Health + Happiness Petal — keeps people from feeling stuck in one place. In an unexpected twist, it also complements work patterns that emerged during the COVID-19 pandemic (while the project was under construction). As people established work-from-home patterns, they quickly discovered the physical and emotional benefits of getting up and moving around rather than staying rooted to one place throughout an entire workday.

In the PAE Living Building, the deckony is the preferred spot for employees seeking a beautiful, airy setting, whether as a backdrop for work or to share a coffee or beer with their colleagues. It is, by design, a programmatic community space.

The deckony invites people in with its sweeping views, abundant fresh air, and indoor-outdoor connectivity. In a sense, it stands as a metaphor for the very building that surrounds it.

The deckony also offers the most dramatic example of a multi-sensorial biophilic environment of any space within the PAE Living Building, ticking off virtually every one of the 14 classic patterns of biophilia identified by Terrapin Bright Green in their 2014 paper titled "14 Patterns of Biophilic Design." From the visual connections to the river and the mountains, the motion of leaves on the nearby trees, the airflow, the presence of natural light, a sense of safety, and even the sense of peril that comes from being five floors above ground, the deckony puts biophilia in full bloom.

"Sustainable strategies come in many forms. Some of the most impactful strategies focus on reshaping how people positively interact with a building's features. That's what we had in mind when we designed the changing staircase lighting. Every day, it gives occupants and visitors an opportunity to win the stair game."

ZACH SUCHARA
Luma Lighting Design

"We were inspired by the legendary Greg Baldwin — the ZGF partner who originally persuaded PAE Founder Pete Peterson to stay in Portland back in 1967 — when we were thinking about the design of these stairs. I remember being in an interview with Greg once when he shared with the owner a vision of 'creating spaces for the intellectual collisions, where people just meet randomly in different parts of a building.' We want everyone to take the stairs in our building not just because they're beautiful and it's healthy, but because you're going to run into someone on the stairs in a way you don't do on an elevator. You're less likely to have your phone in your hand; you're more likely to connect."

PAUL SCHWER
PAE

THE HEALTHY TEMPTATION OF THE STAIRS

There are two sets of stairs in the PAE Living Building, both situated in the core. For fire code purposes, one is accessible from the west side of the structure and the other from the east. While both staircases are beautiful and functional spaces, the east-facing staircase has been designed to entice.

The staircase draws people in from its prominent position near the ground-floor building entrance. With wide wooden treads, broad landings, and dramatic cross-laminated timber (CLT) railings, it invites people to get where they need to be in the building by foot rather than by elevator. Plus, the staircase is generously sized to encourage conversation and interaction among "travelers."

Since it is interior to the building, the main staircase features neither natural light nor exterior views. So the team developed a strategy to allow people to "play" with the building and its lighting via stair use. Sensors integrated into the lobby level count how many people use the stairs throughout the day. Half of the lighting in the stairs uses red, green, blue, white (RGBW) color-changing technology that can be modulated level by level. At the start of the day, the color on the lowest level is set to a deep red, green, or blue color to draw people into the staircase while the upper landings all remain white. As more people use the staircase, the space fills with saturated color. This has two key benefits: First, it makes the healthy stair-versus-elevator choice an easy (and entertaining) one. Second, as colored light increases and white light decreases, it lessens the overall energy used by the stair lighting. Interpretive information near the staircase explains the system, further engaging and compelling occupants and visitors.

The building's central staircase features dramatic CLT railings and a light display that changes color according to usage patterns.

The Health + Happiness Petal: **FEELING FINE**

108

"Another way that the PAE Living Building will promote overall health and wellbeing is by encouraging an active lifestyle and our first floor gym is one way we do that."

NICK COLLINS
PAE

THE FITNESS CENTER

PAE's commitment to its employees' health and wellness also includes a slightly more traditional amenity. A workout room with exercise equipment and shower facilities occupies approximately 1,000 square feet on the northeast corner of the building's ground floor. The space is visible from the street, filled with natural morning light, and directly connected to the bike storage room. It is accessible to all PAE employees, who had a similar feature in their previous Portland location and collectively requested that the center be included in the PAE Living Building plans. PAE rents the fitness center space as part of its overall lease in the building.

109

COVID AS A HEALTH CONCERN

With the start of construction coinciding with the early phase of the COVID-19 pandemic, the PAE Living Building team re-opened design discussions in spring 2020 to determine whether anything needed to change to accommodate infection control considerations.

The project's ventilation strategies already offered an advantage, as the mechanical system provides 100 percent outside air that is combined with the outside air that flows through open windows. No interior air is recirculated. Plus, without recirculated air, infectious particles would have a very difficult time traveling from one floor to another. Still, the team wanted to be absolutely sure that they didn't need to make significant changes to any systems.

After reviewing Centers for Disease Control and Prevention (CDC) guidelines and considering various options, the team determined that very few modifications to the design were necessary. They bumped up the outside air system's quantity slightly and added electrical outlets to the stairwells (unventilated per fire codes) to allow for portable HEPA air filter devices to be brought in if necessary. Otherwise, they felt confident that the original designs would be sufficient to protect occupants from most airborne contaminants.

"Experts agree that good ventilation is the most effective and practical way to rid a space of contaminants. (F)resh air dilutes the contaminants as they move around the room."

WHY OPENING WINDOWS IS KEY TO REOPENING SCHOOLS
The New York Times, 2/26/21

The Health + Happiness Petal: **FEELING FINE**

THE MATERIALS PETAL

The Right Stuff

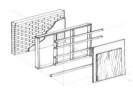

113

The Materials Petal: **THE RIGHT STUFF**

THE MATERIALS PETAL
LIVING BUILDING
CHALLENGE VERSION 3.1

PETAL INTENT

The intent of the Materials Petal is to help create a materials economy that is non-toxic, ecologically restorative, transparent, and socially equitable. Throughout their life cycle, building materials are responsible for many adverse environmental issues, including personal illness, habitat and species loss, pollution, and resource depletion. The Imperatives in this section aim to remove the worst known offending materials and practices and to drive business toward a truly responsible materials economy. When impacts can be reduced but not eliminated, there is an obligation not only to offset the damaging consequences associated with the construction process, but also to strive for corrections in the industry itself. At the present time, it is impossible to gauge the true environmental impact and toxicity of the built environment due to a lack of product-level information, although the Living Building Challenge continues to shine a light on the need for transformative industrial practices.

PETAL IMPERATIVES

- Red List
- Embodied Carbon Footprint
- Responsible Industry
- Living Economy Sourcing
- Net Positive Waste

114

EXPLORING THE MATERIALS PALETTE

Materials are key to the design of any building. In a Living Building, materials selection is often considered the most difficult piece of the overall puzzle. For a Living Building sited in a historic district with strict design restrictions, materials can make or break the entire effort.

The PAE Living Building designers had a great deal to consider when pondering materials options:

CONTEXT. The ZGF architects began by looking to the Skidmore/Old Town neighborhood for inspiration. They studied the surrounding historic structures as well as photographs of the buildings that once stood in the district, which showed that traditional brick, cast iron, and timber were the predominant materials of the day.

COST. Price began to push certain material choices out of the picture. Masonry, for example, was more financially feasible than cast iron. (At one point, ZGF looked at using cast stone panels for the exterior to pick up on the cast iron language used in the district, but even cast stone proved too expensive to meet the building pro forma.)

SIMPLICITY. Less is more in the PAE Living Building. The designers specified as few materials as possible, choosing "ingredients" that could stand on their own — often as exposed finishes (such as the concrete floors and shear walls). Simplifying the overall materials palette shortened the list of products that had to be vetted for Red List compliance while also allowing the beauty of the building itself to shine through.

The Materials Petal: **THE RIGHT STUFF**

"We were never going to do some shiny, mirrored metal building. We started with the district context then narrowed from there. That context pointed us in a direction to explore materials and form."

JUSTIN BROOKS
ZGF Architects

"An ethos that ZGF tries to bring to any project is if a material can do three things or four things or, better yet, ten things, then we want to use it for as much as it can do. If something can be a structural material and a finished material and provide a biophilic connection and allow for change over time, that's a material that we want to pick."

KATHY BERG
ZGF Architects

IMPERATIVE:
RED LIST

To be certified as a Living Building, a project cannot contain any of the materials or chemicals specified in the Living Building Challenge Red List. Version 3.1 of the Challenge, under which the PAE Living Building was registered, restricts the following items (with temporary exceptions made for some chemicals due to limitations in the materials economy):

- Alkylphenols
- Asbestos
- Bisphenol A (BPA)
- Cadmium
- Chlorinated Polyethylene and Chlorosulfonated Polyethylene
- Chlorobenzenes
- Chlorofluorocarbons (CFCs) and Hydrochlorofluorocarbons (HCFCs)
- Chloroprene (Neoprene)

- Chromium VI
- Chlorinated Polyvinyl Chloride (CPVC)
- Formaldehyde (added)
- Halogenated Flame Retardants (HFRs)
- Lead (added)
- Mercury
- Polychlorinated Biphenyls (PCBs)
- Perfluorinated Compounds (PFCs)

- Phthalates
- Polyvinyl Chloride (PVC)
- Polyvinylidene Chloride (PVDC)
- Short Chain Chlorinated Paraffins
- Wood treatments containing Creosote, Arsenic or Pentachlorophenol
- Volatile Organic Compounds (VOCs) in wet-applied products

Working with materials that steer clear of the Red List is always an extremely difficult part of the design and construction process for Living Building project teams. Even when specified materials are kept to a minimum, there are still thousands of individual items and components that must be scrutinized. And that vigilance must be maintained from initial design discussions all the way to occupancy, which can be a matter of years.

The PAE Living Building team called on the experts from the Portland office of Brightworks Sustainability to guide the project's materials vetting process. Brightworks' Jeff Frost and Chris Forney pulled from their experience on other Living Buildings to spearhead the effort, collaborating closely with Integrated Eco Strategy (IES), makers of the Red2Green digital materials tracking platform. (See the next page for more on Red2Green.) Together, Brightworks and IES worked with ZGF and Walsh Construction Co. to determine which products would accomplish all the important project goals: complement the designers' vision, align with the budget, and adhere to the Living Building Challenge.

MATERIALS WAYFINDING

Unlike other green building standards, the Living Building Challenge is non-prescriptive. It is up to each team to determine the most suitable ways to accomplish the Challenge Imperatives given the distinct characteristics of their project. While this approach breeds creativity and innovation, it also means there are few, if any, directly applicable Living Building roadmaps.

In the context of materials, having no instruction manual required every early Living Building project team to re-invent the proverbial Red List wheel, turning the vetting process into a cumbersome and time-consuming undertaking. Information about evaluated products was usually catalogued in spreadsheets, which were woefully ill-equipped to manage the complexity and sheer volume of data involved. These lists were sometimes posted to the Living Building Challenge Dialogue (an online resource available to Living Building project teams interested in sharing knowledge and seeking clarification), but they were specific to individual projects and not always useable by teams working on different building types, in different regions, etcetera.

Then a more sophisticated tool emerged that helped streamline the approach. After supporting several Living Building project teams' materials research, a Massachusetts-based organization called Materially Better (an off-shoot of Integrated Eco Strategy, or IES) introduced the Red2Green digital materials tracking platform in 2015. Brightworks was an early adopter of Red2Green so was well-versed in the software's functionality and value by the time they got involved in the PAE Living Building. As such, this project relied on the Red2Green solution from the very beginning, which proved efficient and cost-effective.

But even with Red2Green incorporated into the process from the start, there was still an enormous amount of research that had to be done for the PAE Living Building. For one thing, the bulk

118

> *"There hasn't been a Living Building project yet that has found a way to avoid thousands and thousands of hours of Red List materials vetting. That means there have been a few hundred projects doing all that heavy lifting versus the hundreds of thousands of buildings that are getting built. So this process is not equitable yet and it's really difficult from a design fee standpoint. This will begin to change as the databases fill out, but it is not yet solved and it needs more time."*

PAUL SCHWER
PAE

> *"When we needed to account for the materials that came on-site, we did a good job getting things into Red2Green, which helped build out that infrastructure. Where there used to be nothing, now there's something so there's value in that. We also modified our punch list software program and used it for checking in materials as they arrived on-site to ensure only approved materials were installed in the building. The system, for all intents and purposes, completes the chain of custody for Red List-compliant materials and includes digital text and imagery. All in all, material management was one of the more difficult parts of the project."*

ED SLOOP
WALSH

of projects whose data was woven into the Red2Green platform were located on the East Coast, making many of their materials less ideal for a Portland, Oregon project (due to distances they had to travel, which would make them undesirable or, if ordered in large quantities, ineligible according to the Materials Petal Living Economy Sourcing Imperative). There was a California Living Building project whose products were cataloged in Red2Green, but most of those vendors were located outside of the maximum distance radius. Seattle's Bullitt Center, only 175 miles away, was within the appropriate range but had been designed and built with materials on the market nearly a decade earlier. More significantly, the Bullitt Center was subject to the Red List from version 2.1 of the Living Building Challenge, which was quite different from what appeared in version 3.1 under which the PAE Living Building registered.

The COVID-19 pandemic exacerbated the vetting process by slowing down and, in some cases, completely interrupting the supply chain, which was especially difficult to accommodate for products that had to be on-site at particular times to align with the construction schedule.

As of June 2021, when the project was nearing the end of its construction phase, a total of 2,737 products had been considered. Of those, 1,778 products were still "Approved for Research" and only 38 products were still "To Be Determined." From this total project-specific database, approximately 25 percent of the selected products were pulled from Red2Green. Although this achievement fell short of Brightworks' goal of 40 percent, it clearly demonstrates the arduous nature of the Red List vetting process. Furthermore, every lesson learned on a Living Building project informs future endeavors. For example, the PAE Living Building made critical contributions to the Red2Green database by adding products and manufacturers from the Pacific Northwest and surrounding regions.

PROCESS IMPROVEMENTS

Nearly every key member of the leadership team involved with vetting materials for Red List compliance had worked previously on at least one Living Building project (although vetting tasks eventually expanded to all of the subcontractors and suppliers, few of whom were familiar with the Challenge). The leaders' experience yielded insights about how to approach the process slightly differently than had been done before, which led to a streamlined system that saved both time and money.

On earlier projects, teams had attempted to pre-vet materials so that products could be pre-approved before being placed into the project specifications. This approach, however, requires project teams to assess far more materials than the number of products that actually get installed on a building.

For the PAE Living Building, the materials team took an alternate approach once the architects had identified the general design palette.

To get started on the materials research effort, Brightworks and WALSH teamed up in April 2019 on high-priority items based on design importance, volume, cost, long lead times, and constructability. Brightworks also got WALSH up to speed on the Red2Green software. From there, WALSH engaged their self-performed trades (earthwork, concrete, and water-resistive barrier work), as well as all critical and complex early trades (plumbing, electrical, mass timber, HVAC, etcetera) in this collective effort. As each trade was brought on board, more products were submitted, researched, and eventually either approved or rejected for use.

The synergy of this teamwork was evident as WALSH became more autonomous in the context of the overall process while

Brightworks stayed focused on product approvals and consulted on the grey areas of the Living Building Challenge Materials Petal. WALSH led the engagement process, Living Building Challenge orientation, and Red2Green training of each new trade that was on-boarded. WALSH also regularly checked the Red2Green and Declare libraries for Red List-compliant options and kept tabs on other resources such as the Red List chemical database and the Living Building Challenge Dialogue for best management practices. (Declare is an International Living Future Institute transparency platform described as a nutrition label for products.)

If Brightworks found non-compliant items on subcontractors' initial material lists, they requested two alternatives as a way to streamline the due diligence process. This system eliminated the need to vet several possibilities for every single product on the specification sheet, which could have amounted to more than 3,000 individual items. So, instead of having to review three options per product type (which was typical on earlier Living Building projects), the PAE Living Building materials vetting team only had to evaluate an average of 2.4 candidates per product type.

"The first question in
materials vetting is the
simplest but the hardest
to answer: What is the
number of products that
will go on the project?
Based on that, you can
start to calculate how many
hours per product will be
spent, which depends on
how many products need
to be vetted relative to
the number that end up in
the building. Is it Three x?
Two x? One x? Ideally, the
first product we identify is
potentially compliant so we
vet that and it makes it into
the project through good
pre-work with the design
and construction teams.
But sometimes there are
limitations in product
categories that means
we have to seek out three
different products."

CHRIS FORNEY
Brightworks

MOVING THE MATERIALS NEEDLE

The underlying intent of the Materials Petal is to reinvent the construction materials economy, encouraging manufacturers to make Red List-compliant products more broadly available as a way of creating a sustainable built environment. This is an undeniably massive goal, but each Living Building — both aspirational and certified — supports the effort by compelling individual suppliers to make healthy changes, however small.

The PAE Living Building helped effect these changes within the materials market:

- **Cascadia Windows** performed testing and expanded the size range of one of its product lines to cover the project's height needs and enable more effective daylighting.

- **Dura Industries** invested in a new Red List-free metal painting system for applying finishes to the building's exterior.

- **Carlisle SynTec** pursued an NSF International drinking water safety rating to ensure that its thermoplastic polyolefin (TPO) fleeceback membrane material was useable on the building's roof, where rainwater lands before making its way to the water treatment system and, eventually, to potable water taps.

- **Several companies** indicated that the PAE Living Building project inspired them to pursue Declare labels, which would better position their manufactured goods in a healthy materials economy for the future. Examples include Structurlam, which received a Declare label for their cross-laminated timber (CLT) and glue-laminated timber (glulam) beams, and Oregon Door, which modified their supply chain to provide materials certified by the Forest Stewardship Council (FSC) for their fire rated doors.

- **Hundreds of manufacturers and suppliers** that submitted products for the first time for consideration on a Living Building project were researched and identified as Red List-compliant, which would most likely deem their products worthy of Declare labels should the manufacturers choose to pursue them. Plus, many manufacturers selected for the PAE Living Building became directly involved in the supply chain engagement process, with a focus on the regenerative and restorative practices embodied in the Living Building Challenge.

122

Main - Partie 2 - 1/50
ca 2743.000 x 175.000 mm
445634 - L1
r = 3891

123

The Materials Petal: **THE RIGHT STUFF**

THE PAE LIVING BUILDING: *Developer-Led, Nature-Inspired*

WHY WOOD

The PAE Living Building was not always going to be a wood structure.

The team also considered concrete and steel for the framework, mapping out the potential impact on costs and schedules for all three. After WALSH put together conceptual estimates for each option, wood won out for several reasons:

AESTHETICS. The architects were drawn to the ways in which wood could blend with brick to fit within the style of the historic Skidmore/Old Town district. Once FSC-certified CLT and glulam beams were selected for the structural framing, wood largely drove the building's design and enhanced its biophilic character.

SOURCING. The team hoped to source the wood from Oregon but discovered that the closest FSC wood supplier that could accommodate the necessary volume for the project was located in southern British Columbia. While not sourced from within the state, the wood still comes from within the Cascadia ecosystem.

CARBON. Of the three materials considered, wood would be responsible for approximately 25 percent less embodied carbon than concrete or steel frames. With wood holding up the structure, the project's remaining concrete (primarily found in the building's core, foundation, and topping slab) accounts for about one-third of the building's embodied carbon.

"The wood in this building does a heavy lift with regard to embodied carbon. By not covering that wood with more finish materials, we avoid canceling out those gains. By not covering things up, there's actually a double benefit. That ethos of just using less stuff is part of the carbon equation."

JUSTIN BROOKS
ZGF Architects

"Even in our mass timber building, concrete has the largest embodied greenhouse gas footprint of all materials; responsible for about a third of the overall carbon. As an industry, as we're trying to reduce the embodied greenhouse gas in our projects, we have to collectively look for ways to eliminate the greenhouse gas emissions from concrete in buildings."

MARC BRUNE
PAE

Wood serves many purposes in the PAE Living Building. It is an artist's medium (here) as well as a source of structural integrity (right).

○ 3,107 mile radius

◐ 621 mile radius

● 311 mile radius

IMPERATIVE:
LIVING ECONOMY SOURCING

This Imperative, which is intended to contribute to healthy regional economies, calls for portions of a project's materials construction budget to come from within specified distances relative to the site. Twenty percent must come from within 500 kilometers (311 miles), an additional 30 percent from within 1,000 kilometers (621 miles), and an additional 25 percent from within 5,000 kilometers (3,107 miles). The Imperative allows for the final 25 percent of a project's materials to be sourced from any location.

At the PAE Living Building, that final "long distance" allowance proved helpful when it came time to specify the toilets. Once the team determined that a vacuum-flush system would be best suited for the project, they went looking for the right fixtures. Their search radius expanded all the way to Norway, where Jets Vacuum AS manufactures vacuum toilets that have the lowest possible flush rate at only one- to three-tenths of a gallon of water per flush (up to 90 percent less water than the 1.6 gallons per flush that is allowed by code). The water-saving benefits of this product choice easily justified the journey the toilets had to take to find their way to the site. (For more on the toilets, see the Water Petal chapter.)

IMPERATIVE:
NET POSITIVE WASTE

One aspect of this Imperative is a requirement that project teams divert specified minimum levels of wasted material during construction. Those minimums, along with the actual percentages achieved by the PAE Living Building, are shown below.

The PAE Living Building team secured access to the adjacent surface parking lot (located directly to the north of the building), where they were able to situate the WALSH trailer and all waste and recycling bins while the project was under construction.

WALSH's Adam Klauba developed a project-specific Materials Conservation Management Plan for the construction phase and oversaw the process of ensuring the project's waste was appropriately diverted to as high a standard as possible. He contacted local haulers, visited multiple waste management and recycling facilities, researched their

procedures and documentation practices, and identified diversion streams for all demolition and construction-related activities that offered acceptable levels of both sorting and transparency.

WALSH also asked all subcontractors working on the project to account for everything that was brought to or pulled out of the site that might not end up in the building — everything from excavated soil to leftover bricks. The point was to divert as much material as possible from the landfill and to recycle, repurpose, or compost through industrial or natural nutrient diversion streams. In a move that exceeded Living Building Challenge requirements and captured its spirit, WALSH also harvested all food waste and composting on-site during the construction phase. As of late June 2021, the project had successfully diverted 1,198 tons of material that would have otherwise ended up in the landfill as construction-related waste.

"We had a whole management plan that was written up around the waste management piece. That's not a brand new thing, but I think we took it to the next level."

ED SLOOP
WALSH

MATERIAL	MINIMUM DIVERSION (%) REQUIRED	MATERIAL QUANTITY REMOVED FROM PROJECT (TONS)	MATERIAL QUANTITY DIVERTED FROM LANDFILL (TONS)	MATERIAL QUANTITY SENT TO LANDFILL (TONS)	DIVERSION (%) ACHIEVED
Metals	99.0%	24.4	24.4	0.0	100.0%
Paper & Cardboard	99.0%	18.4	18.4	0.0	100.0%
Soil (Clean Dirt)	100.0%	334.4	334.4	0.0	100.0%
Biomass	100.0%	4.6	4.6	0.0	100.0%
Rigid Foam, Carpet, Insulation	95.0%	0.0	0.0	0.0	N/A
All Others	90.0%	859.1	844.4	14.7	98.3%

"All Others" includes asphalt, concrete and concrete masonry units, brick, tile, masonry, untreated lumber, plywood, oriented strand board, particle board, gypsum wallboard, glass, plumbing fixtures, windows, doors, cabinets, architectural fixtures, millwork, paneling, electric fixtures, motors, switch gear, HVAC equipment, duct, control systems and switches. All diversion data gathered 8/5/21.

THE EQUITY PETAL

All's Fair

PV arrays installed at Renaissance Commons, an affordable housing community in Portland's Kenton neighborhood, help meet both Energy and Equity goals.

The Equity Petal: **ALL'S FAIR**

THE EQUITY PETAL
LIVING BUILDING
CHALLENGE VERSION 3.1

PETAL INTENT

The intent of the Equity Petal is to transform developments to foster a true, inclusive sense of community that is just and equitable regardless of an individual's background, age, class, race, gender, or sexual orientation. A society that embraces all sectors of humanity and allows the dignity of equal access and fair treatment is a civilization in the best position to make decisions that protect and restore the natural environment that sustains all of us. We all deserve access to sunlight and clean air, water, and soil.

We need to prioritize the concept of "citizen" above that of "consumer." Equity implies the creation of communities that provide universal access to people with disabilities and allow people who can't afford expensive forms of transportation to fully participate in the major elements of society. Indeed, most projects in the built environment greatly outlive the original owner or developer — society inherits the legacies of bad decisions and good decisions alike. Since the act of building is a considerable environmental impact shared by all, there is an inherent responsibility to ensure that any project provides some public good and does not degrade quality of life. Finally, it is essential that we recognize the business practices and welfare of the people that we support as we design and build our developments.

Just, the Institute's ingredients label for social justice, is a publicly accessible label and online database with an official connection to the Equity Petal. Just provides a powerful forum for helping project teams support organizations that share the values of a responsible, equitable living future.

PETAL IMPERATIVES

• Human Scale and Humane Places
• Universal Access To Nature And Place
• Equitable Investment
• Just Organizations

POWER TO THE PEOPLE

The partnership between the PAE Living Building and REACH Community Development's Renaissance Commons is a profound example of a nested Living Building Challenge solution. Installing 215 kW of photovoltaic (PV) panels on a roof at Renaissance Commons to supplement the 133 kW array installed on-site at the PAE Living Building did more than meet an immediate energy need. This energy-sharing strategy also created a permanent connection between a for-profit commercial office building and a local non-profit affordable housing community.

As long as the sun shines, Renaissance Commons gets all of the energy generated by the PV on its site and PAE gets the associated renewable energy credits (RECs). As such, Renaissance Commons can repurpose approximately $20,000 (in 2021 dollars) in funds it would have paid each year to Portland General Electric (PGE) and the PAE Living Building will be able to support a valuable local asset. (The ongoing energy donation is in addition to the ~$680,000 donation of the PV panels themselves and the $90,000 cash donation the ownership group made to REACH to help satisfy the Equity Petal's Equitable Investment Imperative.) In other words, for the foreseeable future, the two projects will share much more than a common electrical grid.

THE PAE LIVING BUILDING: *Developer-Led, Nature-Inspired*

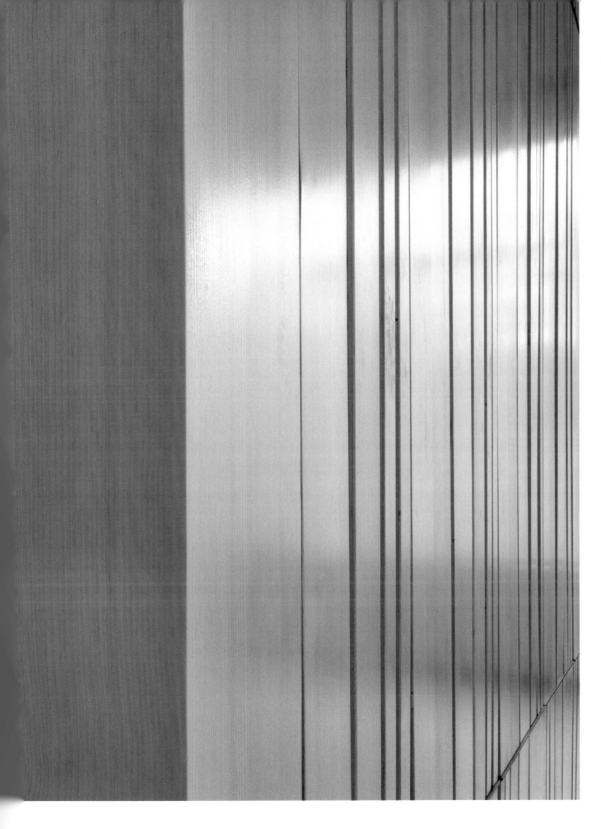

"We need more affordable housing in Portland, particularly in the neighborhood where the PAE Living Building is located. Since Renaissance Commons is five miles away, we think of our new neighborhood as having a five-mile radius rather than a five-block radius. If every building did something like what we did — combining their energy strategies with their social equity missions — we'd literally have dozens of affordable housing projects that wouldn't have to pay for a significant portion of their energy use."

NICK COLLINS
PAE

"By working with REACH to put solar on Renaissance Commons to achieve net positive energy for our project, we are demonstrating a different paradigm that we hope opens the door to net positive energy for more buildings that otherwise couldn't achieve it. We also hope it shows a better way to create a community benefit and environmental benefit with net positive energy development. If you can make it fit in your pro forma, as we did, it's a win-win."

MARC BRUNE
PAE

133

"The PAE Living Building helps PAE's aspirations for equity in our firm and in our community by coupling a building that is designed to provide environmental performance and creating a benefit for all stakeholders. Our employees receive the benefit of working in a building that is very healthy and free of Red List materials. The greater community benefits through the building's energy donations, water conservation, and PAE's local, sustainable design thought leadership."

SHILOH BUTTERWORTH
PAE

"Since securing our Just label, we've seen an impact in day-to-day business operations at ZGF. As a result of reviewing the criteria and evaluating our practices, we've made multiple adjustments to how we source diverse collaborators, where we purchase, and more. It's helping us provide additional and more equitable benefits to better support our community. It's been profound, honestly, how much it has influenced discussion and awareness."

KATHY BERG
ZGF Architects

Organization Name: PAE
Organization Type: Engineering
Headquarters: Portland, Oregon
Number of Employees: 381

Social Justice Indicators:

Diversity & Inclusion
■□□□ Gender Diversity
■■□□ Ethnic Diversity
■■□□ Inclusion
■■■■ Engagement

Employee Benefits
■■■■ Health Care
■■■■ Retirement Provision
■■□□ Family/Medical Leave
■■■□ Training/Education

Equity
■■■■ Full-Time Employment
■■■■ Pay-Scale Equity
■■□□ Freedom of Association
■■□□ Living Wage
■■■□ Gender Pay Equity

Stewardship
■□□□ Local Communities
■■■■ Volunteering
■■□□ Animal Welfare
■■□□ Charitable Giving
■■■□ Positive Products

Employee Health
■■■□ Physical Health
■■■■ Well-Being

Purchasing & Supply Chain
■□□□ Equitable Purchasing
■□□□ Supply Chain

THE SOCIAL JUSTICE LABEL 2.0
PAE-002   EXP. 04/30/2022

INTERNATIONAL **LIVING FUTURE** INSTITUTE™

Organization Name: ZGF Architects, LLP
Organization Type: Architecture
Headquarters: Portland, Oregon
Number of Employees: 776

Social Justice Indicators:

Diversity & Inclusion
■■■□ Gender Diversity
■□□□ Ethnic Diversity
■■□□ Inclusion
■■■□ Engagement

Employee Benefits
■■■□ Health Care
■■■□ Retirement Provision
■■□□ Family/Medical Leave
■■□□ Training/Education

Equity
■■■■ Full-Time Employment
■■□□ Pay-Scale Equity
■■□□ Freedom of Association
■■□□ Living Wage
■■■□ Gender Pay Equity

Stewardship
■□□□ Local Communities
■■□□ Volunteering
■■□□ Animal Welfare
■■■□ Charitable Giving
■■■■ Positive Products

Employee Health
■□□□ Physical Health
■■□□ Well-Being

Purchasing & Supply Chain
■■■□ Equitable Purchasing
□□□□ *Supply Chain*

THE SOCIAL JUSTICE LABEL 2.0
ZGF-001   EXP. 3/26/2022

INTERNATIONAL **LIVING FUTURE** INSTITUTE™

JUST THIS

The last of the four Imperatives listed in the Living Building Challenge Equity Petal zeroes in on organizational culture; specifically, the commitments key stakeholders in any Living Building project make to social justice.

The official language of version 3.1 of this Imperative states, in part:

The project must help create a more just, equitable society through the transparent disclosure of the business practices of the major organizations involved.

PAE was one of the first 100 companies to pursue a Just label, which is the International Living Future Institute (ILFI) transparency platform for organizations interested in revealing and optimizing their social equity policies. Just is a voluntary disclosure tool that the ILFI describes as a "nutrition label for socially just and equitable organizations." ZGF Architects also has a Just label and Edlen & Co. was in the process of working on their submission for their Just application as construction on the building was coming to an end.

To secure a Just label, companies assess themselves according to six measurable categories: Diversity & Inclusion, Equity, Employee Health, Employee Benefits, Stewardship, and Purchasing & Supply Chain.* The results can reveal a lot, including the values companies can be most proud of as well as the areas where they can improve. Whether a Just label is used for introspection or promotion is up to each organization that seeks it.

It is not a fluke that PAE was a pioneering Just organization. Equity and transparency, in addition to thought leadership, have always been key to the company's culture. Now, the Living Building that bears PAE's name is a physical manifestation of those commitments.

*   These categories come from Just 2.0.

136

THE PAE LIVING BUILDING: *Developer-Led, Nature-Inspired*

"One of the unique things about this project team is the number of women who were involved, particularly in leadership roles. I was the principal-in-charge for the developer, the architectural partner in charge was Kathy Berg, the structural partner in charge was Anne Monnier, the architectural PM was Milena Di Tomaso, the lead electrical engineer was Karina Hershberg, the lead mechanical engineer was Katie Zabrocki, the lead energy modeler was Rachel Wrublik. And there were plenty of other talented women in supporting positions who lent their expertise along the way. This project doesn't just stand for what's possible in the built environment; it represents the changing face of our industry."

JILL SHERMAN
Edlen & Co.

Standing in the under-construction cistern, clockwise from lower left: Michaela Zaro, WALSH; Ed Sloop, WALSH; Aubrey Ganz, PAE; Katie Zabrocki, PAE; Zach Suchara, LUMA; Marc Brune, PAE; Nick Collins, PAE; Gabrielle Serriere, PAE; Gauri Vengurlekar, Edlen & Co.; Jill Sherman, Edlen & Co.; Kent Usher, WALSH; Kyle Heckaman, WALSH

The Equity Petal: **ALL'S FAIR**

THE BEAUTY PETAL

Look at That

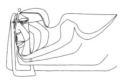

The Beauty Petal: **LOOK AT THAT**

THE BEAUTY PETAL
LIVING BUILDING
CHALLENGE VERSION 3.1

PETAL INTENT

The intent of the Beauty Petal is to recognize the need for beauty as a precursor to caring enough to preserve, conserve, and serve the greater good. As a society, we are often surrounded by ugly and inhumane physical environments. If we do not care for our homes, streets, offices, and neighborhoods, then why should we extend care outward to our farms, forests, and fields? When we accept billboards, parking lots, freeways, and strip malls as being aesthetically acceptable, in the same breath we accept clear-cuts, factory farms, and strip mines.

.PETAL IMPERATIVES
• Beauty + Spirit
• Inspiration + Education

> "*Beauty is part of what makes great spaces and great places but because it's hard to measure, it can get squeezed out to the sides. It's so fabulous that the Living Building Challenge makes room for beauty as part of the story. It's a large part of the delight people experience in Living Buildings; they're responding to the beauty and quality of the space.*"
>
> **JUSTIN BROOKS**
> ZGF Architects

MEASURING UP

The fact that beauty is included among the Living Building Challenge performance areas has been a topic of much discussion since the world's greenest building standard was launched in 2006. Architects, engineers, and others have debated whether something as unmeasurable as aesthetics has a place beside such quantifiable factors as energy, water, and carbon. But those very questions are at the heart of the Beauty Petal, which is designed to elevate the conversation about how the built environment can and should inspire on a purely emotional level.

The International Living Future Institute (ILFI) addresses beauty in version 3.1 of the Challenge this way:

Mandating beauty is, by definition, an impossible task. And yet, the level of discussion and ultimately the results are elevated through attempting difficult but critical tasks. In this Petal, the Imperatives are based on genuine efforts, thoughtfully applied. We do not begin to assume that we can judge beauty and project our own aesthetic values on others. But we do want to understand people's objectives and know that an effort was made to enrich people's lives with each square meter of construction, on each project. This intentionality of good design and graceful execution must carry forth into a program for educating the public about the environmental qualities of each Living Building Challenge project.

The Beauty Petal: **LOOK AT THAT**

"We looked carefully at the proportions of the Fibonacci series and the historic neighborhood. It wasn't with the intent to mimic what happened in the historic buildings; it was an attempt to derive detail and connectivity through those biophilic proportions that are aesthetic and pleasing to the eye — a combination of nature's systems and forms brought together with a very high level of craft."

KATHY BERG
ZGF Architects

"With the Fibonacci cycle of numbers, we get this commonality that connects all of us together in the world. There's a natural draw towards that proportional system because we're all built on that system and so are the living things that are all around us. Using it in this project helped us relate the building to the natural world; it's that biophilic relationship that really drove the organization of the PAE Living Building's architecture."

JUSTIN BROOKS
ZGF Architects

FOLLOWING THE GOLDEN RULE

The architects drew on classic influences and historic precedents to map the key design characteristics of the PAE Living Building.

In its submission to the Historic Resource Review, ZGF Architects wrote: "An overarching proportional system defines the district's architectural character. That system is represented in an articulation of base, body, and top, and has a direct relationship to the golden ratio or Fibonacci series often found in classical architecture, which served as inspiration for the historic district's defining structures."

As they explored the proportions and patterns of the buildings that first stood in the Skidmore/Old Town neighborhood, ZGF found numerous examples of the Fibonacci sequence — also referred to as the golden ratio, the golden section, or the divine proportion (due to its transcendent natural perfection). With its harmonious pattern of squares, rectangles, and circles, the Fibonacci sequence is a series of numbers that provides

the formula for numerous shapes found in the natural world. Beginning with the number zero and continuing infinitely, the sequence is built on the sum of the two numbers that precede any number: 0, 1, 1, 2, 3, 5, 8, 13, 21, 34, etcetera. This formula establishes the mathematical pattern often revealed in nature, such as in rose petals, pinecones, fiddlehead ferns, snail shells, hurricanes, and countless other examples. Human beings have a tendency to respond to and represent these proportions in the things we make — including within the built environment.

The PAE Living Building's carefully chosen materials helped emphasize the desired pattern's visual impact while simultaneously connecting to history and suggesting modernity. Brick, specifically, was the ideal way to articulate it all, infusing the building's façade with detail, richness, light, and shadow.

KEEPING IT SIMPLE

The aesthetic appeal of the building is rooted in its simplicity.

Taking a pared-down design approach served multiple purposes — from minimizing the number of exterior façade and interior finish materials that had to be vetted for Red List compliance to exposing the inherent beauty of the materials used. Adding fewer components and layers allowed the fundamental material palette to prevail.

The architects and engineers shared a philosophy of honoring nature. Just as the building's energy and water systems mimic natural processes, the design aims to reduce the figurative load so nature can do its work. The architecture is driven by the physical properties of how air, water, and sun move in and through the structure, nurturing it and its occupants. The building itself is an ecosystem, efficient and effective because of its very simplicity.

Many of the building's room and hallway dividers (such as shown here, center right) are constructed using vertical elements arranged according to the Fibonacci sequence.

The Beauty Petal: **LOOK AT THAT**

REPURPOSING THE MAPLES

The street trees that had to be removed from the site to make way for construction have found a new home inside the PAE Living Building.

The project team worked first with Epilogue, a local lumber mill committed to keeping removed urban trees out of firewood stacks or wood chip piles. Once the red maples were removed in spring 2020, Epilogue milled them into two-inch slabs. Those pieces were air-dried over the next several months then kiln-dried in early 2021. From there, the wood went to the furniture artisans at ECOPDX who created the new desk and cabinetry that grace PAE's reception area on the building's third floor. (See photo on facing page.) In addition, PAE's

Nick Collins took a break from his engineering duties to build a series of end tables out of the remaining maple. Collins also took some of the boards to the home of ZGF's Kathy Berg so she and her sons could build a project with it.

In all, the sidewalk trees yielded approximately 1,000 board feet of lumber that appears almost blonde in color. Epilogue was able to retain some of the red maples' "live edges," which can also be seen in the beautiful furniture crafted from the urban lumber.

"The furniture we made is really useful and now an integral part of the building. It was fascinating to watch what traditionally would be waste become something of great value. It was nice seeing the trees get a second life."

NICK COLLINS
PAE

WRAPPED IN FIR

A major benefit of a wood-framed building is that the structural system holds it up while also serving as the final finish.

Such is the case in the PAE Living Building, where natural wood hues dominate the interior. Exquisite Douglas fir is exposed everywhere — most notably in the cross-laminated timber (CLT) ceiling and the visible surfaces of the CLT support beams. (In all, the CLT contains five layers of wood, with Douglas fir delivering elegance while spruce and pine lend structural strength.)

The stairways are also rich with wood, helping to draw people in with the undeniable power of beauty. The stair treads themselves are made from six-inch-by-twelve-foot glue-laminated (glulam) beams turned on their sides and the landings are made from CLT. The railings are CLT panels tipped on their sides with Douglas fir visible on both faces to make a visual impact from every angle.

SIMPLE PLEASURES

Elements have been added throughout the building to enhance beauty and elicit human delight, per the Beauty + Spirit Imperative.

LOBBY ART. One of the first things a visitor sees upon entering the PAE Living Building is a sculpture honoring the winds that blow through the Columbia River gorge. The piece connects wind's role in Native traditions with its modern value as a renewable energy source. The wood carving was created by Toma Villa, a Portland-raised member of the Yakama Nation.

FLOOR-SPECIFIC PALETTES. Each of PAE's three floors in the building (levels 3, 4, and 5) has a distinct regional theme, expressed through colors, textures, and imagery. Floor 3 honors the Oregon coast and is accented in shades of sand and shells; floor 4 evokes the Pacific Northwest forests and is awash in greens; floor 5's blues pay tribute to the Columbia River and the Cascade mountains. (For photos of each floor's palette, see pages 97, 140, and 147.)

MURALS. Separate but integrated murals grace the walls on the three levels occupied by PAE. They are immediately visible upon exiting the stairs or the elevator on each of those floors. Created by artist Jessilyn Brinkerhoff, each mural follows a distinct theme drawn from nature, complementing the color palette for that floor and placed according to topography — from coastal to forested to alpine.

DECKONY MIRROR. A mirror stands behind the kitchen counter in the fifth-floor deckony, sporting the profile of snow-capped mountains and a small tree on the slope. The design honors the analogy of a Living Building being like a tree on a mountain — something that can only survive by using the sun, water, and nutrients that fall within its reach. From its spot in the deckony, the mirror not only reflects the expansive views that reach from Skidmore/Old Town to Mount Hood; it also places the humans who stand before it directly in the etched and reflected landscape. (See the photo on page 111.)

The mural on the third floor offers tones of coastal sands and shells.

147

The PAE library, located on the third floor, offers open spaces, plush seating, and pods where people can work on their own or meet with others.

148

"There are many mechanical systems that help this building perform well and integrate with nature. But not everything has to have a purpose other than just being beautiful. Some things in the building are the way they are simply because we wanted a delightful space."

PAUL SCHWER
PAE

"Inevitably, buildings are for people and sustainable lighting design is not just about using less energy. Light shapes the experience of being in the building, so we made lighting decisions holistically to enhance that experience for every user. This holistic understanding of users' needs and the nature of the space allowed us to create a beautifully integrated and effective lighting design that is flexible enough to be used for at least a decade."

ZACH SUCHARA
Luma Lighting Design

CLUES IN THE BRICKS. Subtle adjustments to the brick patterns on the building's east and south façades provide two different data points. Brick ends are rotated vertically at two elevations (three and a half feet and eight feet above sidewalk level) to reveal a pair of high water marks: The first is how high the water rose during the historic Willamette River flood of 1894; the second is the projection based on United States Geological Survey (USGS) data of how high the water could rise in a similar event in the Skidmore/Old Town neighborhood due to climate change. The bricks' coursework serves as a reminder of how climate-responsible design can help protect urban, historic, cultural, and natural heritages.

DISGUISED RP DEVICE. A reduced pressure (RP) plumbing device near the building's main entrance has been cleverly hidden in a planter, which adds a biophilic grace note to soften an important but generally unattractive building feature.

BIOPHILIC ENTRIES. Canopies located at first-floor entries are designed to shed rainwater back toward the building and into open-faced downspouts that channel water into sidewalk-level planters. These features celebrate the rain that nurtures the building, visually display its usefulness, and amplify the trickling sounds of its movement — all of which combines to create small but powerful engagements with nature as people enter and exit the structure.

DECORATIVE ACOUSTIC SUPPORT. In the main PAE conference room and in the deckony space, where noise mitigation is more of a concern, rows of looped fabric acoustic material hang in waves from ceiling tracks. These pieces effectively tamp down the sounds that would otherwise bounce off the enclosed hard-walled spaces without blocking the exposed wood. Plus, they are placed in a pattern that evokes water, providing a gentle biophilic accent. (See photos on pages 105 and 146.)

SPREADING THE WORD

The twentieth and last Imperative of the Living Building Challenge version 3.1 is Inspiration + Education, calling for materials that explain the operation and performance of the project. It is by design that this Imperative, intended to educate, inform, and motivate occupants and visitors, serves as a final punctuation mark within the Challenge. Because Living Buildings are meant not just to be regenerative; they are meant to inspire profound change.

Tours of the PAE Living Building are conducted regularly for members of the public, trade professionals, and local student groups. Interpretive materials found throughout the structure help explain its functional areas and detail its features. In addition to a section of PAE's website specifically dedicated to the building, there is signage containing QR codes that link directly to explanatory information housed online. Among the highlighted interpretive elements are:

THE CISTERN. Information about water storage is posted on a cistern access hatch located in the building lobby. Additionally, ZGF graphic designer Man Hui Chan etched artwork directly into the cistern lid to express the impact a single drop of water can have on a region's overall aquatic systems.

THE WATER TREATMENT SYSTEM. Windows in the ground-floor corridor provide a glimpse of the composters and liquid waste storage tanks, telling the story of how water works its way through the building.

ENERGY USE. The building's energy use and generation data is posted online for educational and tracking purposes.

AN ACADEMIC CASE STUDY. A number of architectural and engineering schools around the country are using the PAE Living Building as one of the case studies in their design classes.

On a higher level, the building itself delivers experiential wisdom — wordlessly, quietly, elegantly. Revealed water and energy systems, a transparent materials palette, and interiors bathed with fresh air and natural light all work together to express the project's intent and help meet the goals of the Beauty Petal.

"I understand the necessity of having additive signage to explain building elements. But I also hope that the timelessness of the materials and the quality of the space is what inspires people to understand that this Living Building is not a science experiment. It's actually a really beautiful, expressive, integrated piece of architecture."

JUSTIN BROOKS
ZGF Architects

PAE's Paul Schwer leading tours of the mechanical room and PV-covered roof.

> *"The city was a really good partner in getting us to a beautiful building. The zoning and development guidelines for the historic district can look onerous, but we had a very successful engagement with Portland's Historic Landmarks Commission that helped us create a building that's of its own time but reflects the time and place of the historic district."*

JUSTIN BROOKS
ZGF Architects

BEAUTIFUL PORTLAND

The City of Portland was instrumental in helping make the PAE Living Building a thing of beauty.

City staff and department representatives worked closely with the project team to ensure that the project honored Skidmore/Old Town's historic past while also standing as a symbol of what a sustainable built environment can look like going forward. This successful collaboration helped lay the foundation for future environmentally-responsible commercial developments in this and other Portland neighborhoods.

The Living Building Challenge is about creating buildings that operate as efficiently and present as beautifully as a flower. What better place than the City of Roses to sprinkle such seeds?

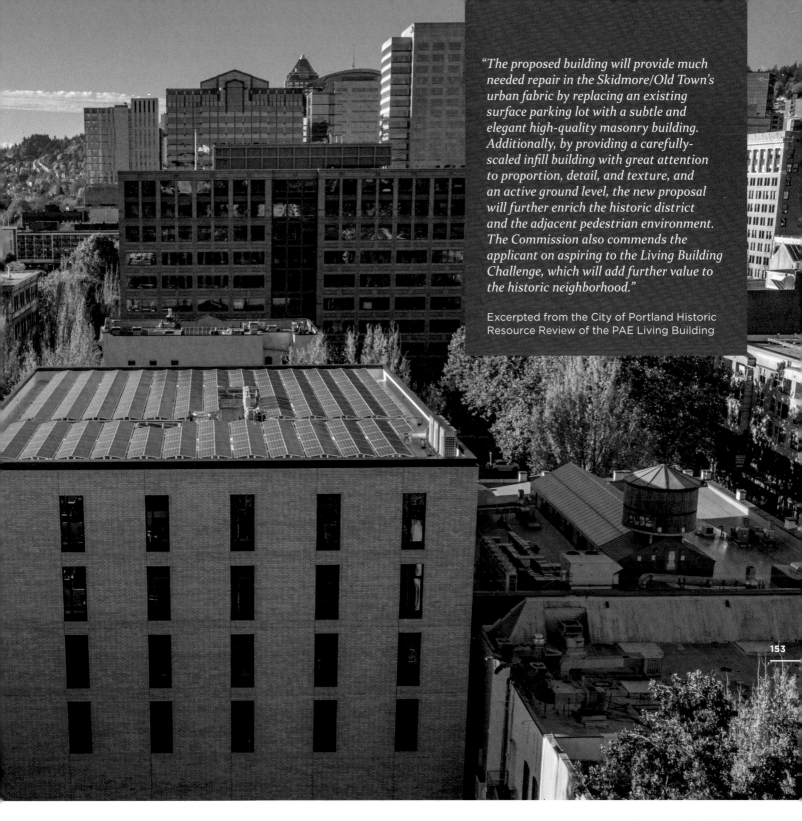

"*The proposed building will provide much needed repair in the Skidmore/Old Town's urban fabric by replacing an existing surface parking lot with a subtle and elegant high-quality masonry building. Additionally, by providing a carefully-scaled infill building with great attention to proportion, detail, and texture, and an active ground level, the new proposal will further enrich the historic district and the adjacent pedestrian environment. The Commission also commends the applicant on aspiring to the Living Building Challenge, which will add further value to the historic neighborhood.*"

Excerpted from the City of Portland Historic Resource Review of the PAE Living Building

The Beauty Petal: **LOOK AT THAT**

WHAT MAKES THE PAE LIVING BUILDING A 500-YEAR BUILDING

	WHY BUILDINGS GO INTO DISREPAIR	HOW BUILDING DESIGN ENDURES FOR CENTURIES
DESIGN	Buildings with no character or that have been mass produced in a "cookie cutter" style hold less value over time and are less likely to be preserved.	The PAE Living Building is designed to be a building that is of its time, but timeless in its response to the historic context. The exterior incorporates the Golden Ratio and the Fibonacci series with a modern take on historical proportions. Inside, the building harnesses the power of biomimicry and modern interior design for optimum occupant health and wellness. The engineering design includes simple systems that are easy to maintain and easy to replace when they reach the end of their life. The design's significance is multifaceted and, we hope, will hold value over time.
CRAFTSMANSHIP + MATERIAL QUALITY	Buildings made from cheap materials, built with poor craftsmanship, or both cannot withstand the rigors of daily use nor the challenges of weather that the building is subjected to over time.	Designed and built by some of the most talented architects, engineers, and contractors in Portland with quality materials, the main structural components are Cross Laminated Timber (CLT) and concrete. Some of the oldest buildings in the world are built from wood and stone (very similar to our structural materials). Some of the oldest wooden structures in the world still standing today are the Horyu-ji Temple in Japan (700 AD) and the Urnes Stave Church in Norway (1132 AD).
RESILIENCY / EARTHQUAKES	Buildings designed to code minimum requirements for life/safety usually must be demolished after earthquakes. While a code building allows for people to safely exit after a major seismic event, the building itself undergoes so much damage that it cannot be repaired economically.	Designed structurally to seismic category IV, the same as hospitals and fire stations, the PAE Living Building is designed to survive very large seismic events and still be repairable. For example, it is designed to withstand an event such as the large Cascadia Subduction Zone (CSZ) earthquake that has a probability of hitting our region every 300 to 500 years.
RESILIENCY / FLOODS	Buildings in or near flood zones can be damaged beyond repair after a flood. This can be due to several factors beyond water damage such as inadequate structural foundations or the sediment and debris impact to the building during or after flooding.	The PAE Living Building is located outside of the 100-year flood zone and within the 500-year flood zone. While water could reach the building's first floor in the second scenario, the damage would be repairable and would not undermine the building's foundation.

154

WHY BUILDINGS GO INTO DISREPAIR	HOW BUILDING DESIGN ENDURES FOR CENTURIES
ENERGY EFFICIENCY — Buildings designed to just meet current energy codes will become more and more costly to operate as energy prices increase. A typical, modern commercial office building lifespan ranges from 50-120 years. In some cases, the costs of making significant energy efficiency improvements to the building façade and mechanical systems becomes so expensive it does not pay back. Eventually, those buildings are torn down.	The PAE Living Building is designed to be one of the most energy efficient buildings in the country. It will be net positive energy, producing 105% of the energy that it uses over the course of a year. The battery storage will also aid in the storage of that energy so that it can be used when needed. Additionally, the goal for the building is to put infrastructural systems in place to ensure it can be adaptable for future systems.
FLEXIBILITY — Buildings designed for singular use that cannot be retrofitted for other purposes due to low floor-to-floor heights have little to no flexibility for the future. Century-old buildings with high floor-to-floor-heights have survived for this reason while buildings of the 1950s-70s with low floor-to-floor heights have not survived.	The PAE Living Building has a 13' - 6" floor-to-floor height on all its office floors and largely column-free areas for significant flexibility for multiple use types and tenants in the future.
LAND VALUE + ZONING — Land value can increase so much that it becomes economically more advantageous to demolish the building and replace it with a new, taller, and larger building on a parcel of land should zoning allow it.	The PAE Living Building is in a historic district that limits the construction and development options for zoning and the building is the largest size allowed in this zone. The current zoning is likely to remain for a very long time compared to other zones because it is in one of the most historically significant areas in the city.
UNIQUENESS — Buildings with little to no historical or cultural significance hold less value and are less likely to be preserved.	The PAE Living Building is the first, fully certified Living Building in Portland, the largest Living Building in Oregon, and one of the largest urban commercial Living Buildings in the world.
LOVE — Buildings are preserved because they are loved.	Some of the oldest buildings in the world are still here today because they are loved. From temples in Japan to the educational halls of Cambridge and Oxford, buildings are preserved because they are loved generation after generation. We hope and believe that the PAE Living Building will be cherished enough to be preserved for many generations to come.

155

A LIVING BUILDING COMPARISON:
THE BULLITT CENTER

DEVELOPMENT

Investment from
Bullitt Foundation

ARCHITECTURE

YEAR CERTIFIED:
2013

RATING SYSTEM:
ILFI Living Building
Challenge 2.0
Full Certification

SQUARE FEET:
52,000

- 6 stories
- External shades
- Triple glazed windows
- Basement
- No dedicated bike room
- Loading dock
- External irresistible stair
- Automated operable windows
- 2 lobbies
- NLT (Nail Laminated Timber)
- 4,100 SF mechanical room + electrical space

STRUCTURAL

CATEGORY:

Code minimum
seismic

Concrete
core along
East facade

Concrete mat
slab, steel and
wood columns

ELECTRICAL

242 KW
Onsite PV system
cantilevered PV
twice the area
of the roof

PV backfeeds
into radial utility
network

16.0 EUI

No Battery / No Micogrid

SITE

where alternatives are commercially available

Does not contain
any Red List
materials*

1 mile from
downtown core
98 walk score

21 bus routes
within 1/2 mile

Local Seattle
beers on tap

LIGHTING

82% of the
building
is daylit

0.4
watts/sf

Energy efficient LED,
fluorescent task lights,
ambient lights

PLUMBING

56,000 GAL
CISTERN IN
BASEMENT

25 TOILETS FEEDING
INTO **10 COMPOST BINS**

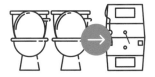

- Foam flush composting toilets removed in 2020 replaced with vacuum flush
- Graywater treatment system filtered by a green roof, infiltrated below sidewalk
- No separate urine collection system
- Rainwater to potable water treatment system
- Annual water use 117,947 gallons per year

HVAC SYSTEMS

Ground source
geo-exchange

Hydronic
radiant floor

Roof mounted
central heat
recovery
dedicated outside
air ventilation

Supplemental
AC: water source
heat pumps
serving radiant
ceiling panel

THE PAE LIVING BUILDING: *Developer-Led, Nature-Inspired*

A LIVING BUILDING COMPARISON:
PAE LIVING BUILDING

ARCHITECTURE

YEAR CERTIFIED:
ESTIMATED 2022

RATING SYSTEM:
ILFI Living Building
Challenge 3.1
Full Certification

SQUARE FEET:
58,000

- 5 stories
- No external shades
- Double glazed windows
- No basement
- Dedicated bike room
- No loading dock
- Internal architectural exit stairs
- Partial operable/manual windows
- 1 lobby
- CLT (Cross Laminated Timber)
- 2,500 SF mechanical room + electrical space

SITE

where alternatives are commercially available

Does not contain any Red List materials*

In downtown core and historic district 99 walk score

23 bus routes 6 rail lines within 1/2 mile

Local Portland beers on tap

PLUMBING

71,000 GAL CISTERN UNDERGROUND

18 TOILETS FEEDING INTO **20 COMPOST BINS**

- Vacuum flush composting toilets
- Graywater treatment system discharged to sanitary waste due to high water table
- Separate urine diversion system
- Urine will be turned into liquid fertilizer
- Rain water to potable water treatment system
- Annual water use 177,854 gallons per year

DEVELOPMENT

Investment from
Multiple Private Investors

STRUCTURAL

CATEGORY:

IV

Same as hospitals & fire stations

Concrete core in center

Concrete mat slab, wood columns, spread footing foundation

ELECTRICAL

328 KW
132.6 kW Onsite
195.4 kW Offsite

125 KW
250 KWH
Battery

Full Microgrid

PV backfeeds into downtown area network electrical grid

18.6 EUI
estimated
includes retail program

LIGHTING

65% of the building is daylit

0.58 watts/sf fully lit

100% LED lighting with nighttime sweeps

HVAC SYSTEMS

Air source heat pump

Hydronic radiant floor

Floor by floor heat recovery dedicated outside air ventilation units

Supplemental AC: Air cooled VRF fan coil units

THE PAE
LIVING BUILDING PARTNERS

DEVELOPER
Edlen & Co.

ARCHITECT
ZGF Architects

CONTRACTOR
Walsh Construction Co.

MECHANICAL, ELECTRICAL, AND PLUMBING ENGINEERS
PAE

ENERGY AND CARBON MODELING
PAE

TECHNOLOGY DESIGN
PAE

LIGHTING DESIGN
LUMA

STRUCTURAL ENGINEER
KPFF

CIVIL ENGINEER
KPFF

WATER TREATMENT (RAINWATER AND COMPOSTING)
Biohabitats

RED LIST MATERIALS RESEARCH
Brightworks Sustainability
Materially Better (from
Integrated Eco Strategy)

LANDSCAPE ARCHITECT
ZGF Architects

BUILDING ENVELOPE CONSULTANT
RDH

REAL ESTATE PARTNER
Apex Real Estate Partners

LANDOWNER
Downtown Development Group

Red maples removed from the sidewalks on the site
found new life as the PAE reception desk (built by
ECOPDX) and a side table (built by PAE's Nick Collins).
The adjacent wall's vertical elements are arranged
according to the Fibonacci sequence.

159

TEAM ACKNOWLEDGEMENTS

PAE | LUMA

*Principal-in-Charge
Core and Shell*
Paul Schwer

*Principal-in-Charge
Tenant Improvements*
Nick Collins

Project Manager
Marc Brune

Mechanical Engineer of Record
Conrad Brown

Electrical Engineer of Record
Grant Parthemer

Mechanical Design Lead
Katie Zabrocki

Plumbing Design Lead
Luke Hendricks

Fire Protection Design
Stuart Graham

Electrical Design Lead
Karina Hershberg

Electrical Design
Craig Collins

*Mechanical Design, Energy
Modeling, Commissioning*
Rachel Wrublik

Mechanical Design
John Sabo

Plumbing Design
Travis Lewis

Plumbing Design
Charles Norris

Electrical Design
Brian Choi

Electrical Design
Kyle Lindsley

Electrical Design
Eric Reed

Electrical Design
Josh York

Energy Modeling
James Cullin

Energy Modeling
Jess Scanlon

*Building Information Modeling
(BIM)*
Aubrey Ganz

*Building Information
Modeling (BIM)*
Joe Delwiche

Environmental Documentation
Karen Joslin

Technology Designer of Record
Steve Kelly

Technology Design Lead
Ryan Sennett

Technology Design
Blaine Parthemer

Audio/Visual Design
Scott Simpson

*Project Coordinator,
Environmental Documentation*
Briana Whitehead

Project Coordinator
Trevor Elvey

Project Financial Analyst
Lisa Delzer Cox

Lighting Designer of Record
Zach Suchara

Lighting Design Lead
Gabrielle Serriere

Lighting Control Lead
Shea Sterner

Lighting Design Lead
Molly Stowe

Lighting Designer
Anna Winn

Communications
Sarah D. Fischer

Marketing
Katrina Emery

Marketing
Julie Satterwhite

Graphic Design Lead
Tara Brooks

Graphic Design
Sarah KC Cowan

Graphic Design
Paula Hopker

EDLEN AND CO.

Development Management
Jill Sherman

Project Conceptualization
Mark Edlen

Financing Lead
Roger Krage

Construction Management
Gauri Vengurlekar

Financing Support
Carly Harrison

DOWNTOWN DEVELOPMENT GROUP (DDG)

Land Investment
The Goodman Family

ZGF

Partner in Charge
Kathy Berg

Design Architect
Justin Brooks

Environmental Graphic Design
Man Hui Chan

*High Performance Building
Specialist*
Chris Flint Chatto

Project Manager
Milena Di Tomaso

Project Architect
Alice Elliot

Interior Designer
Donna Ford

Project Architect
Tiana Kimball

Landscape Architect
Greg Matto

Interior Architect
Michael O'Mara

Specifications Writer
Lona Rerick

Project Administration
Jamie Schoettlin

Project Architect
Curt Williams

KPFF

Structural Principal-in-Charge
Anne Monnier

Project Structural Engineer
Lee Glassford

BIOHABITATS

Senior Engineer
Pete Muñoz

Senior Engineer
Erin English

Senior Engineering Technician
Olin Christy

Engineer / Landscape Architect
Crystal Grinnell

Engineer
Shayla Woodhouse

RDH

Project Principal
Ariel Levy

Project Manager
Casey McDonald

APEX REAL ESTATE PARTNERS

Executive Director
Nathan Sasaki

Supporting Broker
Bruce Garlinghouse

Supporting Broker
Ali Davis

Marketing Support
Emy Lewis

BRIGHTWORKS SUSTAINABILITY

Materials Petal Consultant
Jeff Frost

Materials Petal Consultant
Chris Forney

INTEGRATED ECO STRATEGY

Materials Researcher
Amy Merselis

Materials Researcher
Angela Saltamartini

Project Coordinator
Brenna Irrer

Materials Researcher
Brianna Rousseau

Materials Researcher
Carlye Woodard

Materials Researcher
Christine Osimo

Software Support
Clark Semon

Materials Researcher
Irene Winkelbauer

Data Analyst / Software Support
Jason McNair

Materials Researcher
Kurt Kolok

Materials Researcher
Lisa Carey Moore

Project Coordinator
Luke Tomashek

Project Coordinator
Mariah Kurtz

Project Coordinator
Matt Root

Quality Assurance
Matt St. Pierre

Materials Researcher
Nick Noyes

Materials Researcher
Patrice Cohoon

Quality Assurance
Rebecca McClintic

Materials Researcher
Tyler Boutiette

WALSH CONSTRUCTION CO.

Senior Project Manager/ Chief Estimator
Ed Sloop

Project Manager
Kent Usher

Superintendent
Kyle Heckaman

Assistant Superintendent
Sam Sullivan

Sustainability Coordinator
Adam Klauba

Project Engineer
Steffen Shultz

Project Engineer
Sean Geddes

Project Administrator
Linda Woolery

Quality Assurance Manager
Jake MaManna

Director of Innovation
Mike Steffen

Assistant Superintendent
Vic Lundmark

Layout, Assistant Superintendent
Osmani Gonzalez

Marketing
Maren Sinclair

Project Administrator
Linda Woolery

Closeout Coordinator
Renee Moore

Safety Coordinator
Kirk Chandler

Safety Manager
Nate Ricker

SUBCONTRACTORS

ACADEMY SPECIALTIES, LLC

Project Manager
Jef Kalina

AMERICAN DIRECT

President
Bryon Whetstone

Project Manager
Jeff Nehler

B&B TILE & MASONRY, INC.

President
Kevin Storey

*Estimator/
Project Manager*
Nathan Storey

BLACK LINE GLAZING

Owner / Estimator
Darand Davies

Project Manager
Matt Cannon

Superintendent
Jeff Toth

Foreman
Bill Lee

BRIDGEPORT INTERIORS, INC.

Project Manager
Gilbert Leon

CALPORTLAND COMPANY

CARLSON ROOFING COMPANY, INC.

Project Manager
Greg Carlson

Superintendent
Daniel Munoz

Foreman
Victor Ramirez

CARPENTRY PLUS, INC.

Project Executive
Russ Brotnov

Project Manager
Tim Hanson

Lead Foreman
Jason Fehlman

QA/QC
Levi Brotno

CARRILLO'S JANITORIAL SERVICE LLC

Owner
Juan Carrillo

CASCADIA WINDOWS LTD.

*General Manager -
Construction Services*
Parv Sangha

Sales Representative
Jeff Martin

Project Coordinator
Chris Samra

CONCRETE INSPECTION SERVICES

*Vice President/
GPR Technician*
Collin Bates

DE-EL ENTERPRISES, INC.

DENNIS' SEVEN DEES LANDSCAPING, INC.

DEPAUL SERVICES, INC.

Project Manager
Maria Todd

EAGLE STRIPING SERVICES, INC.

Chief Estimator
Kelly Schafer

EC COMPANY

Superintendent
Shawn Leonard

Foreman
Wade Sparks

*Solar Photovoltaic Design /
Project Manager*
Thomas Farringer

Project Manager
Dennis Sheldon

Account Executive
Ryan Murphree

Technical
Terry Callahan

*Technical Systems
Foreman*
Derek Sayer

*Technical Systems
General Foreman*
Joe Stevenson

ECOPDX

Owner
Eugene Park

GRAYBAR ELECTRIC

SCHNEIDER ELECTRIC

IBEW LOCAL 48 - ELECTRICAL WORKERS UNION

FARWEST STEEL REINFORCING COMPANY

Contracting Manager
Ted Mumford

GEOTECH FOUNDATION CO WEST

Vice President
Steven R. Lundin

HANSET STAINLESS, INC.

President
Luke Hanset

HILLEBRAND CONSTRUCTION, INC.

President / Supervisor
Daniel Hillebrand

Project Manager
Yachin Hillebrand

Project Administrator
Robyn Hillebrand

Foreman
Benjamin Hillebrand

Finisher
Larry Moran

Finisher
Anthony Dominquez

INDIGO PAINT & CONTRACTING

General Manager
Matt Brubaker

MARK NEWMAN ARCHITECTURAL WOODWORKING

President
Mark Newman

MORROW EQUIPMENT COMPANY, LLC

President
Andrew Morrow

NESS & CAMPBELL CRANE, INC. (OR)

Managing Director
Stephen Brazier

*Estimator /
Project Manager*
Bill Chapman

NORTHWEST LININGS & GEOTEXTILE PRODUCTS, INC.

Project Manager
Luai Zureikat

Superintendent
Rogelio Arellano

*Senior Technician /
Lead QA*
Misael Mundo Rosales

Technician #3
Edgar Ortuno

Field Supervisor
Armando Alvarado

NORTHWEST SCAFFOLD SERVICE INC.

PARAGON TILE & STONE, INC.

Commercial Estimator / Project Manager
Brandon Weeks

PAULSON'S FLOOR COVERINGS

Vice President, Commercial Division
Josh Hoffman

Senior Project Manager
Jesse Blevins

Director of Preconstruction
Jesse Hancock

PENINSULATORS NORTHWEST, INC

Design & Development for Venetian Blinds
Sam Blair

Project Manager & Execution of Install of Venetian Blinds
Josh Loret De Mola

PIONEER SHEETMETAL, INC.

General Manager/ Estimator
Aaron Brawner

Project Manager
Kenny Griffith

Draftsman/ Logistics
Mike Holland

Foreman
Anton Bocharov

Apprentice
Dylan Blake

PITMAN RESTAURANT EQUIPMENT

Construction Sales Representative
Danny Slifman

PREMIER PRESS DBA PEP PRINTING INC.

RALPH'S CONCRETE PUMPING, INC.

RDF BUILDERS CO.

President
Tom Mitchell

Earthwork Trade Supervisor
Brad Lewman

Concrete Trade Supervisior
Chuck Howard

Envelope Trade Supervisor
Dalan Askew

Crew Coordinator
Ike Shadrick

Finish Carpentry Trade Supervisor
Mike Bufton

WRB Field Personnel
Doug Dinsdale

Concrete Field Personnel
Jason Trickett

Laborer Foreman
Liz Stewart

Crane Operator
Blondin West

Bellman
Josh Patterson

Carpenter - Concrete Layout
Rick Vanderveer

Layout
Philip Sarono

Concrete Foreman
Rob Bolkovatz

Carpenter - Concrete
Derek Perrin

Carpenter - Concrete
Peter McVeety

Concrete
Scotty Whitwell

Carpenter - Concrete
Charlie Hutchins

Concrete
Anthony Tomisa

Carpenter - Concrete
Abe Andrews

Concrete
Mike McCarthy

Concrete
Donovan Rodrigues

Gate Monitor
Nathan Gilroy

Concrete
Krystal Hugget

Concrete
Jason Bennett

Concrete
Daniel Perez

Carpenter - Concrete
Shane Gill

Concrete
Giovani Valasquez-Ortigosa

Concrete
Alexa Arendell

Laborer - Concrete
Isaac Williams

Laborer - Concrete
Joel Renner

Site Laborer
Justin Waser

Site Laborer
Karen McDaniel

Demo
Charlie Booth

Laborer
Josh Jolley

Laborer
Kevin Granillo

Laborer
Ryan Hienrick

Laborer Apprentice
Kendra Clark

Skin Doctor
Devin Stearns

Carpenter - Concrete
Carlos Flores

Carpenter - WRB/Windows
Keigan McGarry

Carpenter - WRB/Windows
Mike Ferguson

Carpenter - WRB/Windows
Ryan Delihanty

Carpenter - WRB/Windows
Dylan McHargue

Carpenter - Concrete
Jorge Martinez

Carpenter - WRB/Windows
Daniel Boyzo

Carpenter - WRB/Windows
Steven Albert

Carpenter Apprentice - WRB/Windows
Brandon Morin

Finish Carpenter
Travis Goffic

Finish Carpenter
Phat Chu

Finish Carpenter
Kevin Mercer

Finish Carpenter
Tucker Bufton

Finish Carpenter
Joe Klure

Finish Carpenter
Richie Sockchea

Demo Laborer
Dalan Askew Jr.

REPUBLIC SERVICES INC. #472

Construction Account Manager
Greg Pauly

SP PLUS CORPORATION

Regional Manager
Majtaba Ali

STANDARD TV AND APPLIANCE

Project Manager
Cyndi Wilkinson

STRUCTURLAM MASS TIMBER CORPORATION

Project Engineer
Alese Ashuckian

SUSTAINABLE NORTHWEST WOOD

Director of Green Markets
Paul Vanderford

Director of Business Development
Terry Campbell

TERRACALC LAND SURVEYING, INC.

President
K. Jay Pannell

TK ELEVATOR CORPORATION

New Installation Sales Associate
Jordan Mason

Operations Manager
Steve Laiblin

Operations Coordinator
Rick Reddaway

Installation Mechanic & Adjuster
Jake Roake

Installation Mechanic
Adam Alamano

Lead Adjuster
Devon Berns

Adjuster Apprentice
Craig Plummer

Installation Apprentice
John Berokoff

Installation Apprentice
Guy James

**TOTAL
MECHANICAL, INC.**

Project Executive
Daniel Carlson

Project Manager
Wes Bentley

Project Engineer
Kandice Marks

Plumbing Foreman
Travis Spreen

Pipefitter Foreman
Caleb Hamnes

**GARATT-CALLAHAN
COMPANY**

Territory Manager
Travis TadeWaldt

Technical Sales Support
Theodore Lanz

**NEUDORFER
ENGINEERS**

Project Manager/PE
Mike Vawter

*Test and Balance Field
Technician*
Rueben Krasnogorov

**CLIMA-TECH
CORPORATION**

Project Manager
Matt Kraft

**ARCTIC
SHEET METAL**

Project Manager
Ron Hebdon

Project BIM Coordinator
Eric Knight

Foreman
Gary Johnson

Field Crew
Ivan Leonchick

Field Crew
Sean Trevino

Field Crew
Blake Shields

Field Crew
Geno Kiewel

JJ MECHANICAL

**ULTRA QUIET
FLOORS**

Corporate Secretary
Cora Waldroup

Senior Project Manager
Rick Ellison

Project Manager
Patrick Johnson

**UNION
CONSTRUCTION, LLC**

President
Ramon Tapia

Project Manager
Victor Rust

Superintendent
Dennie McKee

Estimator
Bill Juhala

**VALE INSULATION
GROUP, INC.**

President
Noe Gaxiola

**WYATT FIRE
PROTECTION, INC.**

Project Manager
Ken Sutherland

Superintendent
Dave Sutherland

Fire Protection Engineer
Max Colley

Foreman
Nick Arzoian

**ZION
METAL WORK**

Project Manager
Mike Riepma

Lead Welder
Kevin DesJardins

Lead Welder
Christian Lugo

Helper
Rob Cosner

**STONEWOOD
DESIGN**

President
Scott Nyseth

PHOTOGRAPHS
AND ILLUSTRATIONS

Jamie Goodwick / PORTLANDRONE:
Front Cover, pages 1, 12, 13, 17, 18, 23, 25*, 26, 32, 33*, 37,
39, 40, 49, 50, 51, 57, 75, 76, 80, 83, 92, 121, 125, 129, 153
(*PAE infographics with Jamie Goodwick's photos)

Lara Swimmer Photography: Back Cover, pages 52, 53, 63,
64, 72, 73, 85, 86, 89, 90, 93, 95, 97, 98, 100, 102, 104, 105, 107,
108, 111, 130, 132, 134, 139, 140, 143, 145, 146, 147, 148, 149, 159

**Oregon Department of Forestry's publication "The Promise
of Mass Timber":** Pages 7, 8, 11, 43, 44, 113, 114, 116, 118, 123, 124

Nic Lehoux: Pages 15, 71

Sam Sullivan, Walsh Construction Co.: Page 35

Kyle Schwer: Page 136

**"Morning Oregonian" newspaper Vol XLVI. –
No. 14,416 2/20/1907 edition, page 10:** Page 46

**"The Grand Era of Cast-Iron Architecture in Portland"
by William John Hawkins, page 175:** Page 47 (bottom)

"Portland Then and Now" by Dan Haneckow, page 10:
Page 47 (middle)

Stock: Pages 54, 59, 60, 142, 144

Unknown source: Page 47 (top), page 51 (arches)

164

THE PAE LIVING BUILDING: *Developer-Led, Nature-Inspired*

INTERNATIONAL LIVING FUTURE INSTITUTE

The International Living Future Institute (ILFI) is a hub for visionary programs. ILFI offers global strategies for lasting sustainability, partnering with local communities to create grounded and relevant solutions, including green building and infrastructure solutions on scales ranging from single room renovations to neighborhoods or whole cities. ILFI administers the Living Building Challenge, the environment's most rigorous and ambitious performance standard, as well as the Living Product Challenge and Living Community Challenge. In addition, ILFI offers transparency labels through Just, Declare, and Reveal. Zero Energy, Zero Carbon, and Just 3.0 certification, and Living Future Accreditation are also available. Additionally, ILFI is home to Ecotone Publishing, a unique publishing house dedicated to telling the story of the green building movement's most innovative buildings, organizations, thinkers, and practitioners.

LIVING BUILDING CHALLENGE

The Living Building Challenge is the built environment's most rigorous performance standard. It calls for the creation of building projects at all scales that operate as cleanly, beautifully, and efficiently as nature's architecture. To be certified under the Challenge, projects must meet a series of ambitious performance requirements, including net zero energy, waste, and water, over a minimum of twelve months of continuous occupancy.

ECOTONE PUBLISHING

Ecotone Publishing is the non-profit publishing arm of ILFI and a key component of ILFI's Communication strategy for sharing expert information about green building technologies and design innovations to create a Living Future. As a publisher, Ecotone produces educational case studies, technical knowledge on renewable energy, plus regenerative and biophilic design, and is the leading source of published information about Living Buildings worldwide. Ecotone also offers professional publishing services to help design firms and organizations document and share their stories, lessons learned, and design solutions with others who are also seeking to address the climate crisis and have a positive impact on their communities.

MORE BOOKS FROM ECOTONE PUBLISHING

Ecotone publications are available online at the Ecotone Bookstore at **living-future.org/bookstore** and at other select retailers.

All proceeds from book sales go to supporting ILFI advocacy and programming.

THE LIVING BUILDING CHALLENGE SERIES

THE LIVING BUILDING CHALLENGE
by Mary Adam Thomas

BUILDING IN BLOOM
by Mary Adam Thomas

LIVING BUILDING EDUCATION
by Chris Hellstern

GENERATION GREEN
by Michael D. Berrisford

DESERT RAIN HOUSE
by Juliet Grable

THE GREENEST BUILDING
by Mary Adam Thomas

BROCK ENVIRONMENTAL CENTER FOR A LIVING CHESAPEAKE by Juliet Grable

REGENERATIVE RETROFIT
by Juliet Grable

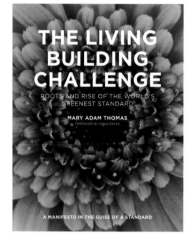

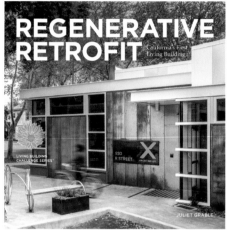

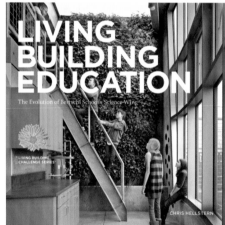

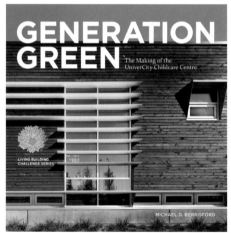

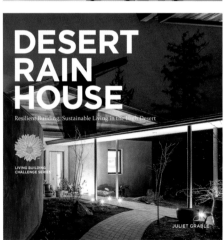

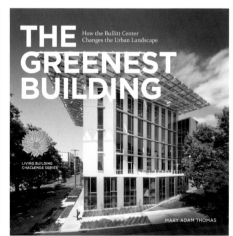

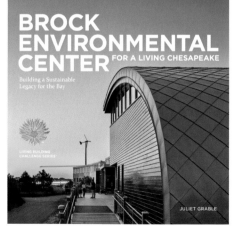